PROLOGUE

The Redford rail smash was a bad business. On that cold November morning, glittering with sunshine and a thin layer of snow on the fields, the London-Manchester express hit a wagon that had strayed on to the main line from a siding. Engine and two first coaches were derailed; scattered cinders set fire to the wreckage; and fourteen persons in the first coach lost their lives. Some, unfortunately, were not killed outright. A curious thing was that even when all the names of persons who could possibly have been travelling on that particular train on that particular morning, had been collected and investigated, there were still two charred bodies completely unaccounted for, and both of women.

Behind the second coach the force of the collision was not felt so disastrously; there were several casualties in the third, but in the fourth, which was a restaurant-car, occupants escaped with a shaking.

As usual on such occasions there were heroic incidents. Conspicuous among these was the behaviour of one of the restaurant-car passengers, a middle-aged man, who jumped down to the track within a few seconds of the impact, and began work of rescue amidst the piled up and already burning debris. Five persons, it was afterwards computed, owed their lives to his gallantry, nor could he be persuaded to desist until his arms and hands were badly burned, and all hope of saving further lives had clearly to be abandoned. Passengers and railway officials alike were limitless in his praise--"He was like a fury," one said, "dashing into the flames again and again, just as if they weren't there--it seemed impossible that one man could do so much in so short a time."

The following day was Sunday and Armistice Day, and the newspapers were naturally full of stories of the disaster and of its hero. He had collapsed, it was reported, after his efforts, but letters and papers in his possession revealed him to be the Reverend Howat Freemantle, a dissenting minister in Browdley, Lancashire. Interest in him was further stirred by the disclosure, made by his wife, who was telegraphed for and arrived later in the day, that he had been travelling alone. This seemed to set his heroism on a higher pinnacle than ever; Mr. James Douglas made it the theme of a long and moving article; and a chorus of adulation rose from all parts of the country. For, as one 'leader' put it: "Many doubtless would have done as much for their loved ones, but this man's devotion and self-sacrifice were for complete strangers, and in this he showed himself magnificently worthy of his profession. In these days, when so much is heard of the failure of organised religion to attract the masses, the selfless bravery of this Nonconformist clergyman strikes a note that will echo far beyond the thunder of rival sectaries."

The Reverend Howat Freemantle spent a week in hospital, and for a few days there were fears that he might have to lose one of his hands. Meanwhile the gaze of the whole country was on him, for the Press, with that capriciously epidemic enthusiasm that partly leads and partly follows the mood of its registered readers, decided unanimously that he was the 'big news' of the moment. Photographs of him, looking tired and rather sad in his hospital bed, appeared on front pages; his face was impressive and thoughtful, and it was even commented by some that he had 'the eyes of a saint'. Of the disaster and of his own exploits he would say not a word--a pathetically understandable attitude in a man in whom modesty and horror were doubtless equally profound. When at last the announcement was made that his hand might, after all, be saved, and that he would soon be fit to undertake the journey to Browdley, the sentimental heart of the newspaper-reading public gave a great upward leap.

That journey home was rather like the return of a wounded victor after a successful military campaign. Hundreds cheered him as he walked from the ambulance to the train at Redford; and by courtesy of the railway company his coach was sent on a through line to Browdley Station, where he was welcomed by the Mayor and Corporation, the Salvation Army Silver Prize Band, and a crowd estimated at nearly five thousand. It had not been realised, however, that he was so ill; and as he was helped down the station slope by his wife and sister-in-law, the Mayor hurriedly cancelled a prepared speech and substituted a few short sentences of praise and welcome. Even the cheers of the crowd were hushed by the man's tragic appearance, and his words, "Thank you all--very much," were clearly heard amidst an awestricken silence. But the cheers swelled out again as the ambulance passed through the narrow streets to the Manse.

The massed limelights of the Press then focused themselves upon that middle-sized manufacturing town, of which few persons in other parts of the country had ever even heard; and it was soon discovered that in the Reverend Howat Freemantle Browdley had possessed no ordinary minister. Everywhere citizens and chapel-goers testified to his generosity, his kindliness, and his devotion to good works, while it

AND NOW GOODBYE

GOODBYE

JAMES HILTON

CONTENTS

PROLOGUE 5

CHAPTER ONE - MONDAY 9

CHAPTER TWO - TUESDAY 36

CHAPTER THREE - WEDNESDAY 52

CHAPTER FOUR - THURSDAY 62

CHAPTER FIVE - FRIDAY MORNING AND AFTERNOON..... 68

CHAPTER SIX - FRIDAY TEA 79

CHAPTER SEVEN - FRIDAY DINNER 89

CHAPTER EIGHT - FRIDAY EVENING.................................... 97

CHAPTER NINE - SATURDAY MORNING 113

EPILOGUE 132

was recalled that during the War he had served in Gallipoli as an ordinary soldier and been wounded twice. Nor in Browdley had he con-confined himself to strictly professional work; his sermons had been eloquent, but he had also identified himself with local literary and artistic societies, the League of Nations Union, and other movements. Newspaper interviewers, unable to approach the man himself (he was confined to his room and could see nobody), found his wife and sister-in-law most gratifyingly ready to answer questions; among other matters it was revealed that his stipend was a very poor one, and that, like so many other clergymen in industrial districts, he had for some time been hard put to it to make ends meet. In particular, he could barely afford even the most urgent repairs to the large, red-bricked residence with which an earlier and more prosperous generation had burdened him. Such facts, together with an insurgent wave of popular emotion, prompted a leading daily newspaper to open a fund for the provision of 'some tangible expression of nation-wide esteem'. Headed by a contribution of fifty guineas from the proprietor, Sir William Folgate, it speedily reached a sum of nearly eleven hundred pounds, a cheque for which was eventually handed to Freemantle at a special meeting convened in Browdley Town Hall. He was still suffering then from the effects of a complete nervous and mental breakdown, and could not make more than a very short speech of thanks. The money, he said, would be devoted entirely to local charities.

But this was by no means the only tribute paid to his heroism. A certain Miss Monks, aged eighty-nine, who belonged to Freemantle's chapel, was so deeply overcome by reading newspaper accounts of how the minister had behaved that she died of heart failure; whilst another old lady, who lived at Cheltenham, and had never even seen Freemantle, offered to pay for the education of his children. He had none, as it happened, of school age, so that the lady's beneficence was frustrated; but he was able to accept Sir William Folgate's three months' loan of a luxurious villa overlooking the sea at Bournemouth. It should perhaps be added that he received many anonymous gifts, among them being an Austin Seven car, which had to be sold, since neither he nor any of his family could drive.

One of the many disclosures made by Mrs. Freemantle to an interviewer had been that her husband's hobby was the composition of music. The enterprising journalist had wished to know more of this, so she had hunted up as many of her husband's compositions as she could find and handed them over. Among them was one, dated 1909, which for some reason attracted more attention than the rest, and within a few days Mrs. Freemantle received an offer from a firm of publishers. But she was unwise enough to hold out for too high terms and negotiations finally broke down, with the unfortunate result that none of Freemantle's music has yet been made accessible to the general public.

By the time the minister and his wife returned to Browdley the following April the whole affair had been almost completely forgotten, and even at Browdley station there was no one to meet them except Mrs. Freemantle's sister. But the Manse, when they reached it, was not quite the same as before; it had been painted inside and out, and there was new linoleum on the floors, and in the minister's study a small bust of Beethoven, which had been accidentally smashed during the renovations, had been replaced by a large silver-framed photograph of Gipsy Smith, subscribed for by the Young Men's Bible Class.

CHAPTER ONE - MONDAY

The Reverend Howat Freemantle awoke about the usual time on Monday morning of that second week in November. From habit, as soon as he was completely conscious, he lit the bedside candle, glanced at his watch ticking loudly on the table, and then at his wife, whose huddled back and deep regular breathing presented a familiar picture close by. Seven-thirty. He reached out an arm to light the gas-ring under the kettle--a manoeuvre dexterously performed as a result of long practice. Then he leaned back to doze for those last and frequently most delightful minutes.

But this morning they were not particularly delightful. Parsons, he had often reflected, were not immune from the 'Monday morning' feeling--on the contrary, they were subject to a peculiarly distressing Monday morning feeling of their own. After Sunday, with its sermons and services, Monday came, not as the beginning of a six days' holiday, as so many lay persons imagined, but as a sudden drop to the bottom of a hill which had to be slowly and laboriously climbed over again.

And it had been a difficult Sunday, he recollected, dark and foggy all day, with congregations and collections very small--serious matters to a Nonconformist minister in a northern manufacturing town already impoverished by the trade slump and unemployment. The chapel, too, had been bitterly cold, owing to an ancient and defective heating apparatus (soon, however, to be replaced), and the fog and chill had got at his throat and given him acute pain during the evening service--'*that* pain', he had already begun to call it in his mind. Curious how people could stare at him up there in the pulpit, and not know that the chief thought in his mind all the time was--'I've got the most frightful sharpness in my throat--wonder if anything serious starts like this?'

When the kettle began to boil he warmed the teapot, put in the tea, and poured. Then, reaching out further, he gave his wife's shoulder the gentle shove which was nearly always sufficient to wake her. She stirred, opened her eyes sleepily, and gave an incoherent murmur. "Good morning," he said, with a smile at her huddled shoulders. He did not look at her face. He felt, though he scarcely admitted it even to himself, a reluctance to observe her during those first few inelegant moments after waking--with her hair crimped up in clusters of curlers, her skin greasy with perspiration, and her lips dry and parched through breathing through her mouth. She could not, of course, help all that; the fault, he knew, lay with himself--in a certain initial fastidiousness which, he feared, was hardly less a sin for being involuntary.

She did not reply to his 'good morning' except by further murmurs, and after a little pause he poured out a cup of tea and placed it on the table next to a novel by W. J. Locke which she was in the course of reading. Then, after putting on an old brown dressing-gown, he poured two other cups and carried them out of the room, across the landing, and into another room where his daughter Mary slept. She was a thin-faced, sallow-complexioned girl of twenty, working as a teacher in the school that adjoined the chapel. He lit the gas and wakened her now, according to established routine; he liked that early morning habit of tea and a chat. He began desultorily to mention politics (there was a by-election pending in the neighbourhood), though he had not uttered many words before he felt again that sharp, cramping sensation in his throat. Mary, however, was not interested in politics, and plunged into chapel and school matters with a briskness that made him, as for relief, pull aside the curtains and see the pale grey dawn outlining the roofs and factories of Browdley; there was no fog, but a soft slanting rain. Then she asked if he would 'hear some Latin verbs she had been learning by heart; she was cramming for a degree examination, and had to make use of every odd moment. He agreed, and for the next five minutes stood solemnly and shiveringly by the window with the text-book in his hand (she had slept with it under her pillow), while she went through the various moods and tenses of the third conjugation. "Rego, Regis, Regit..." How chilly it was, he reflected, and there would be no hot water in the bathroom (the kitchen fire was always allowed to go out on Sunday afternoons), and the smell of bacon was drifting up the stairs just as it had done for goodness knew how many years--did there await him, he wondered, some glorious morning in the dim future, an alternative breakfast smell that would amaze and delight his nostrils? Not that he disliked bacon, or would have preferred any other dish for breakfast; it was in atmosphere rather than actuality that something in him craved for a change..."Regimus, Regitis, Regunt."...He must call and see Mrs. Roseway some time today, and perhaps young Trevis as well--oh yes, and Councillor Higgs about the Armistice Day service. "Well, there you are !" he exclaimed brightly, when she had finished. "You seem to know them all right. Now we'd better hurry up and dress, or else Aunt Viney will have something to say to us when we get down."

Half an hour later breakfast at the Manse began--Quaker oats, bacon and eggs, toast and marmalade--the whole rather carelessly prepared by the maid-of-all-work, Ellen, whose intelligence was so far below normal that Aunt Viney, in her more blustery moments, usually referred to her as 'that half-wit'. But then, you could never get satisfactory servants in Browdley, and Aunt Viney, with or without the slightest encouragement, would tell you why. It was because of the dole, which enabled out-of-work factory hands to live in luxury (silk stockings and lip-stick, Aunt Viney said) while honest people searched vainly for 'good girls to train'.

Aunt Viney (short for 'Lavinia'), viewed in the grey daylight that came in through the dining-room window, was always a rather imposing spectacle. She was fifty-one years of age, and had large staring eyes, quick bustling movements, more than a tendency to stoutness, a menacing optimism that was not quite matched by a sense of humour, and the most decided opinions upon everything. She was an excellent 'manager', and for more than a decade had lived at the Manse with her sister and brother-in-law and their children (there had been boys at one time), looking after them all with undoubted if rather relentless competence. Mrs. Freemantle, it was generally known, was 'not strong', but happily there was no such fragility about Aunt Viney. Vigorous in body and mentally impervious, she knew exactly how to control the children at a Sunday School treat, she could organise round games at a Missionary bazaar, prepare tea for seventy at the Women's Annual Social, win the egg-and-spoon race at the summer outing, turn away the crowd of mendicants who knocked at the door of the Manse--and all with that same air of confident downrightness. She entertained a just slightly contemptuous admiration for Howat. In truth she had never really managed to like Browdley (she was Kentish by birth), and when, on holiday at Southport or Llandudno, she saw sleek, well-dressed parsons playing golf or motoring in smart-looking cars, she often wished that her brother-in-law, with all the brains he was supposed to have, had belonged to one or other of the wealthier denominations.

This morning, as on so many other Monday mornings, she faced the oncoming week with a nonchalant glint of her prominent blue eyes. Breakfast was her particular scene of triumph, since Mrs. Freemantle took hers in bed, rarely appearing downstairs till the morning was well aired. Aunt Viney poured out tea with a steady hand, rebuked her niece for grumbling at the bacon (it was abominably cooked, she perceived, and privately made up her mind to have a real good row with that girl Ellen afterwards), and watched the progress of her brother-in-law's breakfast with managerial solicitude. He seemed to her exactly as she had always known him at breakfast times--quiet, good-tempered, perhaps a little dreamy. Over the Quaker oats he opened his private letters, slitting the envelopes with the knife he would later use for the bacon. Over the bacon and eggs he talked a little, and after that, during the hurried moments before his daughter left for school, he glanced through the *Daily News* and mentioned a few odd things that were happening in the vast world outside Browdley. All this was perfectly according to custom.

From nine till eleven every morning, except Sunday, the Reverend Howat Freemantle was to be found in his 'study'. During those two hours he answered letters, planned addresses and sermons, interviewed callers, and (if he had any spare time left over, which did not often happen) read books and the more serious type of periodicals. The study was a moderate-sized and rather gloomy room on the ground floor, overlooking a tiny soot-blackened front garden. A dozen years ago it had been furnished by Mrs. Freemantle, who had modelled it upon that of her father, himself a dissenting preacher; and Howat, who had no especial preferences in furnishing, had been content to leave it undisturbed from that primal exactitude. There were books, of course-- shelves of them--his own training college textbooks, and stacks of theological works inherited from his father-in-law. There was a pedestal writing-desk, a swivel desk-chair, and a pair of ragged leather armchairs. Two black and white lithographs, one of "Dawn" and the other of "Sunset," embellished alcoves on either side of the fireplace; a many-volumed series of the Expositor's Bible (a gift from his first chapel) occupied a frontal position above the mantelpiece; and a bust of Beethoven (many visitors thought it was Luther) stood on the top of a bookcase containing the latest edition of the *Encyclopedia Britannica*, on which Howat was still paying monthly instalments. Apart from the Beethoven bust the room was impeccably what Mrs. Freemantle had originally planned it to be--the sanctum of a dissenting minister of the more 'thoughtful' type. Its composition as such was far too massive to be overlaid by any freakishness of personality, and all that Howat's occupation ever inflicted on it was a merely surface litter that Aunt Viney easily and regularly cleared away.

Passing along Browdley High Street, and then up School Lane beyond the tram junction, the pedestrian reaches the Manse, after a short and rather depressing walk through a district given over to factories and slum property. There is a privet hedge along the street frontage, but it is low enough for a vague interior view of the study to be available to anyone who deliberately stares, and the Reverend

Howat Freemantle must often have been seen at work there during the last dozen years, especially in winter when it is so dark as a rule that the lamps have to be lit.

On that Monday morning in November Howat lit the single gas-burner over his desk and gave his morning's mail a second perusal. Besides a bunch of obvious-looking circulars there were three private letters, the first from a firm of engineers in Queen Victoria Street, London, confirming an arrangement by which he should call at their head office on the coming Friday to consult about a new heating apparatus. For his chapel members, after freezing and catching influenza for several successive winters, had at last decided to spend money on such an unspiritual but none the less necessary object; sixty pounds had already been subscribed, and there would be a bazaar or something to raise whatever extra might be required. To Howat had fallen the job of going to London to make final arrangements; of course he knew nothing at all about central heating, but his congregation had the usual optimistic belief that a parson must know something about everything.

The second letter was from a well-known missioner, offering to conduct a week's revival in Browdley for twenty pounds *plus* his hotel and travelling expenses.

The third letter was from another London address--Wimpole Street. It fixed an appointment for the Reverend Howat Freemantle to see Doctor Blenkiron at 4. p.m. that same Friday. Howat turned it over rather awesomely in his hand; he had somehow nourished a slender hope that his little plan to fit in a visit to a London specialist might not have succeeded. However, there it was; Blenkiron could see him, even at such short notice, and no one at home, for the present at least, need be told anything about it. It was not only that he was anxious not to worry them--he was equally anxious that they should not worry him. He knew from frequent observation how magisterially Aunt Viney took command of other people's illnesses; she was always so noisily optimistic about them, and at the same time so full of parallel anecdotes of persons who had either died lingering deaths, or had cured themselves by Christian Science or herbs, or some other specific in which Howat had no particular faith. She had, too, a robust common sense which would certainly have made her point out the absurdity of his paying hard-earned guineas to a London specialist before Ringwood's verdict, which could be obtained for as many shillings, had been even asked for. Nor could Howat say precisely why he was unwilling to consult Ringwood first--except that Ringwood was a

.

personal friend as well as a family doctor, and he shrank, somehow, from the human touch in such a business.

Ah, he told himself a shade irritably, throwing the letter into the fire, he was getting nervy--mustn't think any more about it--wait till Friday, anyhow. Plenty of jobs to be done meanwhile. There was the address on Mozart he was due to deliver at the Young People's Guild that night. Fortunately he knew a good deal about Mozart--no need to prepare anything especially. He might carry over his portable gramophone and a few records...He took the remainder of his correspondence to the fireside and pencilled a few memoranda on the back of a circular. Mozart...There was a Trio in E Major he might play over and also, of course, the overtures to "Figaro" and the "Magic Flute ". His eyes brightened a little at the prospect, and he stared across the room to observe, without irony, the view through the window of dilapidated slum cottages overtopped by a five-storeyed cotton-mill. Then, in a mood almost of abstraction, he began to open the circulars hitherto neglected. One was from a tailoring firm in London, advertising a sale of lounge suits at five guineas--to be had in either black or 'clerical grey'. Well, perhaps on Friday, if he could find time, he would call and see about it--he certainly needed a suit badly enough...Another circular was from a firm of outside stockbrokers in Leicester, recommending shares in a brewery. A third was from an ecclesiastical supply stores in Paternoster Row, offering a job line of individual communion cups. A fourth came from Boston, Mass., and accosted him with a list of pertinent questions--"Are your sermons full of pep? Are you sure you are delivering the goods? Are you satisfied with your freewill offerings? Do you feel tired Sunday nights? Are you inclined to be low-spirited, diffident, disheartened?" And for a twenty-dollar course of ten lessons it could all, apparently, be put right.

Howat read through the enclosed and illustrated brochure, but did not tear it up afterwards as he had done the other advertising matter. Instead he put it away in the middle drawer of his desk; it would do for Ringwood to see some time--he would be amused.

Still with the trace of a smile he tore open one of the remaining envelopes. A coloured picture dropped out and fell at his feet, making a little patch of brightness on the drab carpet. He picked it up, guessing it to be a sample sent him by some firm of art publishers--Raphael's "Saint Catherine of Alexandria", he recognised, for he had often admired the original in the National Gallery. The reproduction pleased him, and he was still examining it when he perceived a handwritten note in the envelope. It was just the shortest of messages--"Dear Mr. Freemantle, I am afraid I shall not be able to come for a

14

lesson on Tuesday, as I shall be out of Browdley that day. I saw the enclosed in a shop recently and thought you might like it. Yours sincerely, Elizabeth Garland."

His first thought was that he would have an extra free hour on the following day. Every Tuesday for some months past he had been giving lessons in German to Miss Garland, the daughter of his chapel secretary. It was a means of adding to his rather poor income, besides which it meant rubbing up his own knowledge of German, which was good for him. She was a pleasant and intelligent girl, and had seemed to pick up the language quite satisfactorily; still, he could not but feel grateful for one engagement less during a more than usually crowded week.

He studied the picture again and reflected that it was kindly of the child to have sent it him--yes, very kindly. There was something boyish and simple in him that showed instantly when anyone gave him anything, or even thanked him; he was always pleased in a rather bewildered kind of way--bewildered because he quite genuinely could not think what he had done to deserve it.

He put the picture on the mantelpiece, and several times looked towards it with pleasure during the clerical tasks that kept him employed during the next hour or so. Finally Aunt Viney came in, saw it, and smiled steadfastly while he explained the circumstances of its arrival. "Very kind of her indeed, Howat," was her verdict at length, "but are you quite sure it is very suitable? After all, it looks rather a Catholic picture, don't you think?"

Perhaps it was, he admitted, and put it away in a drawer. As a Nonconformist clergyman he could not be too careful.

Punctually at eleven he put on his overcoat and hat (an ordinary dark grey and somewhat shabby felt) and went out into School Lane. There, in the murky daylight that was only a degree brighter than the gloom of the study, it was possible for one to observe him in some detail. Tall and slim-built, with just the very slightest stoop of the shoulders that suggested thoughtfulness, he was, beyond doubt, fine-looking, and would have been conspicuous among his fellows even had his collar not buttoned at the back. His hair was touched with silver over the temples, but otherwise he looked younger than his age, which was forty-three. His eyes were grey, deep-set, and very bright; he had a strong, rugged profile, and an expression which, in its stern setting, was rather astonishingly winsome. Dr. Ringwood often told him he had missed his vocation in being a parson--he should have been an actor. "With that face you could have been the answer to the maiden's prayer," he used to say, and Howat was always, beyond his amusement, a little puzzled, and beyond his puzzlement, a little grieved. There seemed such a lot of irrelevance in the world. He was dimly aware that he might be considered not bad-looking, but, so far as the matter affected him at all, he found it rather tiresome. Some of the girls at the chapel, for instance, whenever there was a bazaar or a social--so silly and pointless, all that sort of thing. Anyhow, he had never tried to trade on his looks, and most certainly never attempted any gallant airs.

Proceeding along School Lane he entered the High Street. It had stopped raining, but the roadway and pavements were covered with a film of brown mud which glittered in the light of some of the shops. The sky was already yellowing into a kind of twilight; probably there would be fog again later on. People passed dimly by with a nod or a greeting--women doing their marketing, unemployed men lounging around, business folk bustling about the town, and so on. He had to keep his eyes well open--people were so offended if he didn't see them, they were always prone to think he had cut them deliberately. Whom should he visit first? Higgs would be at his place in the High Street; Mrs. Roseway lived over at Hill Grove; there was young Trevis in Mansion Street, close by. Better leave Mrs. Roseway till afternoon-- she wouldn't like him to call before everything in the house had been put to rights', though, Heaven knew, he wasn't the man to notice whether things of that sort were right or not. Young Trevis then, it might as well be; and he was walking briskly along with this intention when a little girl suddenly ran up to him. "Please, Mr. Freemantle, Aunty says will you come and see her at once, as she's been took very had in the night."

He stared down with a kind of surprised vagueness and then identified the child as Nancy Kerfoot, one of his Sunday School youngsters. Her aunt, he knew, was Miss Letitia Monks, and lived in the end house in Lower George Street. "Very well, my dear," he replied. "Run along and tell your Aunty I'll come."

It wouldn't do to ignore a summons of that sort, despite the fact that he had been abruptly sent for by Miss Monks on several previous occasions. She was a character, the old lady, and he had always rather liked her, despite the fact that her piercing voice, her equally piercing eyes, her stern old-fashioned principles, and her quite spotless four-roomed cottage in which she lived on a very few shillings a week, made him feel uncomfortably like a large fly in the presence of a small but exceptionally strong-willed spider. There was something indubitably wonderful about her, he felt; she was eighty-nine, and had never been further away from Browdley than Blackpool. Moreover, she had worked in the same cotton-mill for half a century, had invested all her savings in that same cotton-mill, and during the last few years had lost the greater part of them.

He hastened towards Lower George Street, and outside the end house saw Ringwood's battered Morris-Cowley. As he approached, Ringwood himself came out of the doorway--an elderly, apple-cheeked, rather shrewd-looking general practitioner.

"Hullo, Freemantle. You been sent for too?"

"Yes."

"Go along then. Mustn't keep you. It's no false alarm this time, I'm afraid."

"You think not?"

"Bet you a shilling not."

Ringwood was always outrageously flippant about death. The other clergy in the town did not care for that, or for him either, but Freemantle found it an oddly bearable trait. He half-smiled, nodded, and passed through the open door into the front parlour which had never, he supposed, been used except for funerals, weddings, Christmas and other exceptional occasions. The fender was crowded with huge brass fire-irons that gleamed through the shadows as he passed to the narrow steep staircase beyond. A woman, doubtless a neighbour, called to him to come up. He obeyed, feeling his way in almost complete darkness, and was at last manoeuvred into a very small, hot, and dimly-lit bedroom.

Miss Monks was the oldest member of his chapel; she had belonged to it ever since its opening in 1860. She had regularly attended services twice every Sunday until quite recently; she had given generously to all chapel funds and charities; nor, during her prime, had she ever shirked personal duties. But that was only one side of the picture. For over four decades--ever since most people could remember--she had constituted herself a sort of super-authority to which all chapel questions must in the last resort be submitted. She had waged bitter and incessant warfare against anything and everything new, different, or experimental, and it was hardly an exaggeration to say that she had driven several parsons out of the town, and at least one into a home for the victims of mental breakdown. Of Freemantle himself she had misgivings, but they were weaker ones; and this was partly because she was getting old, partly because he was tactful, and partly (though neither she nor he realised or would have admitted it) because she was attracted by his face.

His eyes, accustoming themselves to the dimness, observed the shrivelled cheeks and piercing eyes that confronted him from the head of the bed. "Good morning, Miss Monks," he began, stooping slightly. His greeting, rather huskily spoken, filled the room with its deep resonant tones--he had a magnificent voice (Ringwood had once said--"It's so damned easy to listen to you talk that one sometimes doesn't bother what it is you're saying"--and he had never felt quite the same about his own words after that). The neighbour passed him a chair and whispered loudly in his ear: "Doctor says she won't last out the day."

"Ah," he answered vaguely, seating himself at the bedside and gazing at the subject of this despairing prophecy. He was, he was aware, a little terrified by Miss Monks. He was just wondering whether she were fully or only partly conscious when she startled him by croaking suddenly: "Very poor attendances there must have been at chapel yesterday, Mr. Freemantle."

"Yes," he admitted, fidgetting under her glance. "The weather, you know, was most unfortunate. I suppose one really can't expect people to turn out in thick fog."

"In my young days people wouldn't have let that keep them at home on a Sunday."

It was her favourite theme, and he gave her the cue she wanted. "Ah, Miss Monks, I'm afraid this is a slacker generation altogether."

She talked for a few minutes as she enjoyed talking, and as he knew she enjoyed talking. The conversation touched upon the question of Sunday games in the parks (soon to come before the Borough Council again), and the forthcoming service on Armistice Day. She was, of course, a bitter opponent of Sunday games, and as for the Armistice Day affair, she had doubts as to the wisdom of those so-called 'undenominational' ceremonies, at which parsons of all creeds appeared together on a single platform. "Safer to keep ourselves to ourselves," she declared, with a tightening of wrinkled lips.

After a time talking seemed to tire her, and Howat was just beginning to think he might decently take his leave when she whispered, with a kind of sinister pride: "Doctor says I won't last out the day."

"Oh, dear me, what nonsense!" The exclamation came out trippingly. "I'm sure Dr. Ringwood never said anything of the sort, and even if he did--"

"He *did*," she insisted, in such a way that further conventional protests found themselves checked at source. She added hoarsely: "Perhaps we could have a prayer together, Mr. Freemantle."

"Why, certainly."

And he bent his head into his hands (Miss Monks would have thought any more abject posture idolatrous) and began to pray. He felt a little unnerved by it all. It was so difficult to think of anything really suitable. What *could* you say to the Almighty by way of introducing an old lady of eighty-nine who was perfectly certain of going to Heaven and equally certain that Heaven was full of marble and white tiles, like a combination of underground convenience and fish-shop? And all the time he was speaking he knew too that Miss Monks was listening with the air of a connoisseur; she felt herself in no pressing need of his interpolations on her behalf--she was merely trying him, seeing what he could do, enjoying a luxury to which she considered herself entitled.

That, he felt, was the worst of being a Nonconformist parson-- in the last resort people didn't need you, they felt themselves able to get just as near Heaven on their own. Not that they probably couldn't, but still, if they thought that, why bother to keep a parson at all? As some species of communal pet, perhaps. It was different in the Roman Church, where people really believed in priestly functions. And again, as often before, he wished there were some ritual for such occasions as this...What could he say, anyhow?...Yet, to his considerable surprise, he heard himself saying all kinds of things, quite eloquently and not at all insincerely; he really meant every word of them--the poor old creature was dying--there had been something rather grand and magnificent about her--he was stirred, touched, and aware that his voice was vibrating with emotion. And when at last he raised his head there were actually tears in his eyes.

"Thank you, Mr. Freemantle," said Miss Monks rather in the tone of an examiner to a student who has done passably well in a *viva voce*.

He bade her a kindly farewell, and held her thin hand for a moment. The stuffy air inside the room (all the windows closed for the past dozen years, he guessed) and the smells of drugs and bedclothes made him feel a little faint. His throat too, was giving him pain again. After a few conventional courtesies to the woman who had shown him up, he descended the stairs and passed out gladly into the street.

Too late now to call on young Trevis; he had to see Higgs the councillor, and there wouldn't be time for both visits. He hastened out of Lower George Street and into the High Street again. Higgs was an optician, who had an office and consulting-room on the first floor of Bank Buildings, just above Phillips's gramophone shop. He was a clever fellow, not yet thirty, the youngest and in many ways the ablest of the local Labour Party. Self-educated, he had worked as a mill-hand while studying for the examinations that entitled him to set up in business. He never attended a place of worship, but had once surprisingly turned up at a series of lectures Howat had given on music. The relationship between the two men was cordial up to a point, and then sharply antagonistic.

Howat felt still somewhat exhausted as he walked along the passage by the side of the gramophone shop, and climbed the stairs to the first floor. He rang the bell and Higgs himself answered it. "Oh, Hullo, Freemantle--glad to see you--do come inside." Howat did not in the least mind being called Freemantle' without the 'Mister '--indeed he rather preferred it--but he could not help reflecting that at Higgs's age he should never have had the nerve to leave out the prefix with a man nearly twice as old...Nerve, that was it--and Higgs had plenty of it. Cool-headed fellow climbing steadily up the ladder which began with a seat on a local council and ended, quite possibly, at Westminster. He was determined to get on in the world, and Howat liked him for it.

"Good morning, Higgs. I hope I'm not interrupting--I thought I'd better call where I'd be sure of finding you."

"Quite right. Do take a chair. I've an appointment in ten minutes, but I daresay he'll be late."

"Well, I don't suppose my business will take more than the ten minutes in any case. I only wanted to know the plans for the Armistice Day service."

"Ah, yes. There's been the usual fuss about it, you know. Or perhaps you don't know. Doxley of the Congregationals thought it was unfair for the Baptist fellow to be given the opening prayer two years in succession. So we've given him the opening prayer instead. The Vicar of the Parish Church, of course, does the address--that seems to be generally agreed upon. Then there's the second prayer--Salcombe rather wants that. Unfortunately that means you'll have to take the hymns, as you did last year and the year before. I don't know how you feel about it--if you object, then Salcombe will have to take his turn with the hymns, whether he likes it or not, only he's not so good at the job--fusses with the tuning-fork for about five minutes before he can get the note--I daresay you've seen him."

Howat smiled. "I don't mind what I do--I'll fit myself in just wherever's convenient. As it happens, I have absolute pitch, so I don't need a tuning-fork."

"Absolute pitch? What's that?"

One thing in Higgs that always especially attracted Howat was his eagerness to assimilate any casual scrap of knowledge that might come his way. He answered: "It means that if I want a certain note--

middle C, for instance--I know it, instantly, without having to think. Nothing very unusual a good many people can do it."

"I see. A sort of gift? Must be very useful. You're fond of music, aren't you, Freemantle?"

"Yes, extremely."

"I think I'm beginning to be, too. When I've time to spare I sometimes go down to the shop below and play over records. I like Bach." He pronounced it 'Back' and added: "By the way, how should one say that fellow's name--was I right?"

Howat replied: "Well, I think 'Bark' is nearer the German pronunciation. But you don't need to be too particular. Far more important to enjoy him."

"Far more important to enjoy everything." The youth's face clouded over with a look of half-truculent eagerness. "Which reminds me, Freemantle, there's that Sunday games question coming up before the Council again. I suppose it's no use trying to persuade you to come over to our side?"

"No good at all," Howat answered, with a shake of the head. "And you ought to know better than ask, after that last argument we had."

"The trouble is, that last argument didn't convince me. And not only that, but it didn't convince me that it convinced you, either."

"Come now, that's too subtle for a parson on Monday morning."

Higgs leaned forward and tapped Howat's knee with his forefinger. "Look here, why can't you be serious about it? I've always had a sort of feeling you were the only parson in the town there was any hope at all for."

"That's very flattering."

"I mean it sincerely, flattering or not. We Labour fellows constantly find you on our side in all sorts of things--the housing question, unemployment grants--oh, any amount of matters that crop up. What we sometimes wonder is why you don't come over to us altogether. Frankly, we'd welcome you just as wholeheartedly as we respect you now."

Howat smiled, but rather wearily. He was in no mood for a political argument, especially with such a notoriously adroit debater as Councillor Higgs. He said, quietly: "I don't really believe that parsons ought to identify themselves entirely with any political party. It's quite true that I often find myself on your side. On the other hand, I sometimes don't, and what would you have me do then?"

"Well, we'd try to convince you. This question of Sunday games, now--"

"My dear chap, I'm not going to go over all that again with you. My position is exactly the same as it was last year--in such a matter I regard myself as the delegate of my congregation, and as they're overwhelmingly against the idea, there's nothing more to be discussed."

"I always thought a shepherd led his flock, not was led by it."

"Don't you think a shepherd would be foolish if he led both himself and his flock over a precipice?" Howat's voice became more animated. "Why don't you try to understand my position? I hope--I even try to believe--that I do some good in this town. Amongst other things, I try to broaden people's minds--I'm keen, as I daresay you know, on literary societies, debating clubs, music, the drama; anything that I think will get and keep people out of the commonplace rut. If I step warily, I may succeed--indeed, I sometimes feel that I am succeeding. But if I were to back you up in supporting Sunday games, I should merely split my congregation, smash up all the good work I'm interested in, and--quite likely--make my whole position in Browdley an impossible one. Do you think that would really be the best thing that could happen?"

"Yes, since you ask me, I do. It's the only course I'd honour you for. As it is, I know for certain what I'd for a long time suspected-- that you're secretly on our side, but haven't the courage to stand with us." His voice rose excitedly, and after a pause for breath he added quickly: "I'm sorry, Freemantle, I really don't mean to be insulting at all--I'm only being as frank as I know how."

"Yes, I quite see that." And at the back of Howat's mind was the thought: I've said too much, somehow or other; I oughtn't to have let myself be enticed into an argument with this fellow--Heaven knows where it will lead to, or what tales he'll spread about afterwards...Higgs was one whom eloquence always stirs to greater eloquence. He went on: "I wouldn't mind so much if your people were all as virtuous as they pretend to be. But they're not. Look at the Makepeaces, the Battersbys, that dreadful old Monks woman--are they *really* the moral cream of Browdley society? Oh, and Garland the draper--mustn't forget *him*. He's the chap who shakes hands at your chapel door after Sunday services--the 'right hand of fellowship', isn't that what you call it? There's not much fellowship about him on weekdays, I can tell you. We're on to him now about some cottages he owns in Silk Street; the rain comes in at all the roofs, but he won't do any repairs--we're trying to make him, but he's got a cute solicitor. I suppose, though, since he's a pillar of your chapel, this kind of talk must sound rather offensive?"

Howat thought despairingly: I mustn't argue, whatever happens; the rain comes in at my roof too, by the way; Higgs and Garland are natural enemies, and I'm not going to interfere between them...He said: "It doesn't strike me as particularly offensive, but that's not to say I'd consider it good taste to join in a discussion of individual chapel members with outsiders."

"Have a look at those houses in Silk Street and see things for yourself"

"Well, I might do that."

"Good of you if you do. And I don't mind a bit being called an outsider. Perhaps you'll feel one yourself some day, so far as the chapel's concerned. The fact is, this town's sunk in narrow-mindedness, and it really makes a fellow sick sometimes to find out what he's up against. And I can't help feeling, too, that the sort of chap in these days who wants to do real good, to improve and elevate people and all that, doesn't find much scope or encouragement in the church. The church, if he lets it, will just use him up, waste his energies, and cramp him all the time. He can find better machinery elsewhere. There's dirt and hypocrisy in politics, I admit, but I think on the whole it gives bigger opportunities."

Howat smiled again. "Perhaps so, perhaps so. But I sometimes wonder whether the people who live most usefully of all are neither parsons nor politicians, but just ordinary folk, like village postmen and engine-drivers and charwomen. It's an interesting question, but I mustn't wait to argue it--I've already taken up far too much of your time, and I'm pretty busy myself, too...It's settled, then, that I take the hymns?"

"Yes, if you will. Thanks for making so little trouble about it. And as for the Sunday games--"

"You'll find me, I'm afraid, ranged alongside my brother ministers. Perhaps that will make you reconsider the comparison you made between me and them--I hope it will, anyway."

They both laughed and shook hands cordially, and Howat went down the stairs to the street with a feeling of almost reluctant liking for the young; councillor. Dangerous, though, to say too much to him...It was becoming foggy, as had seemed likely, and through the yellow gloom came the muffled chiming of the parish clock--a quarter to one. He hurried, so as not to be late for his midday dinner.

Monday's dinner at the Manse was always predictable; it consisted of the remains of Sunday's joint minced into a sort of rissole and warmed up. Howat had had this so often and so unfailingly that it seemed now, by sheer familiarity, to have become appropriate--it both smelt and tasted, somehow, of Monday. He did not, however, bother a great deal about food, which was perhaps as well in the circumstances. He was not even aware that a few minor ailments from which he had suffered at times during the past dozen years had all been dyspeptic in origin.

Dinner was served for four, since by that time Mrs. Freemantle had dressed and come downstairs. She was a thin, angular woman with everything rather sharp about her--her nose, her chin, her cheekbones, her eyes, her way of moving about, and her voice and speech. She was the youngest of her family, while Aunt Viney was the eldest, and despite a difference of physique which could hardly have been greater, there was yet an obvious sisterhood between them. They might bicker when they were alone (indeed, they sometimes did), but whenever they were together they had an air of being ranged four-square against the rest of the world, even when the rest of the world consisted only of Howat. Their dispositions were complementary rather than similar; Aunt Viney could bluster, fly into tempers, and shout; but Mrs. Freemantle's voice, even in most perturbed moments, never rose above a high-pitched and hurried wail.

Howat was always extremely thoughtful and polite to both of them, and submitted good-humouredly to their varying attentions. It was Aunt Viney who sewed buttons on for him (when she remembered), cooked, ordered from shops, and did the more domestic work of the household; in a shadowy way, if ever he were inclined to be irritated by her, he could always reflect comfortingly that she worked very hard, and that no one could imagine what they would all do without her. For his wife, of course, he had tenderer feelings, and if ever she were a little trying he always remembered how highly strung she was, and that quite small things were apt to upset her in a way that she couldn't really help.

This particular Monday dinner found both Aunt Viney and Mrs. Freemantle a little cross, the former from a noisy and indeterminate quarrel with the servant which had been in progress; most of the morning, and the latter because the roof of one of the bedrooms was leaking again and the builder, in her opinion, couldn't have done his job properly when last he had come to repair it. But she was the kind of woman who could never he satisfied with saying a thing once; she had to talk rapidly and indignantly about the leaking roof for over ten minutes, while Howat listened with sympathy tempered by the knowledge that the roof always would leak till it was overhauled thoroughly,

24

and that such an operation would cost more than he was ever likely to be able to afford. His stipend was just under three hundred a year, and though both his wife and Aunt Viney had small incomes of their own, there was really nothing like enough for the upkeep of so big a house. He himself would have preferred to move into a much smaller one, but his wife would never listen to the suggestion, and always talked of any residence less in size than the Manse as 'one of those poky little working-class houses'.

During or just after the midday meal it was Howat's habit to outline and discuss with her some part of his daily routine; he did this even when it was an effort, for he believed it his duty to let her share in all his affairs. He hardly realised that she had other and more satisfying points of contact with the small world of Browdley, and that a good deal of his well-meant conversation bored her. It bored her now, for instance, when he began to talk about the address he was going to deliver that evening on Mozart. He began to sketch out a plan of his ideas, and as often happened when once he began, he went chattering on, with slowly mounting enthusiasm, till Mary began to fidget and his wife to exchange supercilious glances with her sister. Their private opinion was that ideas might be all right for the platform or pulpit, but were hardly suitable for the dinner-table. In the end Mary neatly torpedoed the monologue by enquiring the date of Mozart's birth. Howat, after a rather vacant pause, said he didn't know exactly, but he fancied it must be somewhere about the middle of the eighteenth century. They were all very much amused at his confessed ignorance, and Mary rejoined pertly: "You know, dad, I think you always go far above people's heads when you talk to them about music. Why don't you tell them the useful facts--when he was born, when he died, the names of the things he wrote, and so on?"

Howat answered: "Yes, of course--I ought to include all that, I admit."

"Anyhow," added Mary, "I don't suppose it matters a great deal, for if this fog keeps on, there won't be more than half a dozen there."

Howat nodded and stared blankly at the window, where yellow was already merging through orange to grey.

It was too foggy, indeed, to go visiting in the town that afternoon, especially with the excuse of his bad throat; so he spent a pleasant couple of hours in the little school associated with his chapel. It was a second-rate school, doomed, no doubt, to extinction when any enterprising education policy should take possession of the Browdley authorities; but that day was unlikely to happen soon. Architecturally the school was hopelessly out of date; its rooms were small and badly lit, its corridors long and draughty, and its playgrounds mere patches of wasteland strewn with ink-black cinders. In this establishment there were three classes, the senior in charge of the headmaster, a Mr. Wilkinson, and the two junior ones taught by his daughter and another young woman.

He first of all, as a matter of courtesy, paid a visit to Mr. Wilkinson. Wilkinson was a shabby little man with a pompous manner and a very large, pale, and flabby nose. He experienced certain difficulties of discipline, of which both he and Howat were well aware, but of which they both steadfastly pretended not to be aware; the wastepaper-basket in his room was usually sticky with the remains of half-sucked sweets which, from time to time, he made his pupils disgorge. (Howat would never have known this but for a complaint by the caretaker's wife.) After spending a few perfunctory moments in the senior room, Howat passed on to his daughter's, and here, indeed, his pleasure began. For he liked children, with an intensity that was no affectation; he often thought: If I were not a parson I should like most of all to be a schoolmaster. It was true enough, in a way, though, on reflection, he recognised that he would never have made a very good schoolmaster. He would always have shrunk from teaching the dull stuff that had to be learnt. Besides, he had the most preposterous ideas about education--preposterous, he was prepared to admit, from any normal parent's standpoint. As it was, he could put his theories into strictly limited practice with the certainty that as soon as he was out of the school the teacher would undo any harm he might have perpetrated.

His daughter was pleased to let him take the class for a time, since it gave her extra moments to work at her Latin verbs. He began by walking round amongst the desks and observing what the children were doing; it was a geography lesson, apparently, and most of them were laboriously copying a map of Ireland out of ancient and very dirty text-books. He asked one boy why they were doing this, but the boy said he did not know. Then he began to talk to the boy, at first in an undertone, but later, without definitely realising it, in a voice to which all the class soon came to listen. He asked if anyone had ever been to Ireland; none had; then he asked if anyone had ever crossed the sea in a ship. And from that he progressed to a general talk about islands, and then islands very far away, and then uninhabited islands, and soon he was off on one of those extraordinary impromptu stories which he enjoyed just as much as did any of his listeners. This one was about two small boys sailing across the sea in a small boat, and coming to a land where nobody from England had ever been before. Howat then went to the blackboard, wiped out a careful list of exports and imports which his daughter had drawn up, and began to sketch a map of this strange land just as it came to the knowledge of the two boys. First the vague outline of the shore in the distance, then a narrow river inlet leading into the heart of dense jungle, and so on. Mountains, lakes, and vast swamps all figured in the boys' wanderings, and as each exciting adventure happened Howat marked it down on the board. By the time that the young travellers had lost themselves in the midst of a forest infested with giant spiders and boa-constrictors, the whole class was in a ferment of excitement, as was Howat himself; for half an hour during that November afternoon Browdley did not exist for some four dozen of its inhabitants; the fog and the cotton-mill across the road were lost behind a blaze of tropic sunshine. When at last the school-bell rang, Howat stopped as one disturbed suddenly from a dream; he seemed to recollect himself and added, in an ordinary voice: "Well, boys and girls, that's all to-day, I think. Perhaps I'll tell you more about what happened to the two boys some other time. I hope you know now something about maps, anyhow." But it was a lame excuse; he didn't particularly hope they did, or care whether they did or not; his aim had been different--something not very easy to put into words--something, indeed, which he was never quite sure of understanding himself.

After he had gone his daughter resumed her work of teaching. She had been glad of the interval's respite, though she always said that after her father's intervention a class was completely ruined for the rest of the day.

Howat usually ignored afternoon tea, though if he were out visiting and were offered it, he would accept. He preferred, however, when he was at home, an uninterrupted hour by the fire before his 'proper' tea--a meal which consisted as a rule of tea and an egg. After this there was often another gap of an hour or so before the beginning of evening engagements.

On this unpleasant November day Howat occupied both odd hours in reading a book which would have deeply shocked ninety per cent of his congregation had there been the slightest possibility of their understanding it. It was Jeans's "The Universe Around Us," borrowed from the local library, which had obtained it at his own request.

As Mary had predicted, there was only a very small attendance at the Young People's Guild that evening. The Guild was one of Howat's pet institutions; he had founded it himself some half-dozen years before, and it had flourished, he ventured to think, as handsomely as could have been expected. It met weekly during the winter months; in summer there were country rambles, visits to places of interest, and so on. It had always been Howat's idea to make it a centre of secular enlightenment (backgrounded, of course, by the chapel atmosphere); most of the weekly talks were on literary, musical, or artistic subjects--very few were definitely religious. This aspect alienated the sympathies of some of the older people, who thought that Howat was coddling the young and shirking his plain job of rubbing religion into them. Howat, though, did not care about that; if there were ever to be a choice (though there would not be if he could help it) he was all out for the young; the old, he felt, were so confident of attaining Heaven that they could look after themselves.

As founder and president, Howat always opened the terminal session by an address on some subject or other; it also fell to him to fill in any gaps made by speakers dropping out after the programme had been made up. This November Monday was one of these gap-filling occasions, his talk on Mozart being in lieu of a paper on modern town-planning by a young local architect.

The place of meeting was a bleak schoolroom furnished and panelled in pitch pine--a very hot room at one corner near a stove, and very cold and draughty elsewhere. Nothing relieved the brown varnished monotony of the walls except a map of Palestine and a tattered and faded temperance banner. A desk stood on a slightly raised platform, and on the desk lay a Bible, a hymn-book, and a carafe of water. (The room was used regularly for Sunday School and other chapel functions.) There was also a cupboard which, when incautiously opened, usually emitted a cascade of ragged hymn-books and tea-party crockery. Two inverted T-shaped gas-brackets shed a hissing illumination over the rather melancholy scene, and this evening wisps of fog curled in fitfully when the green-baize doors opened from the vestibule.

Howat gazed with a certain dreamy satisfaction on the dozen or so young persons who comprised his audience. In some ways they satisfied him as much as a far larger gathering; because he could think of most of them individually, knowing their names, homes, and circumstances; and he could marvel a little at the spirit that had brought them out, on a foggy night, to hear him talk about Mozart. Surely he was not wrong, at such a moment, in thinking that he was accomplishing some kind of good in Browdley, that his years of persistence were bearing fruit after all? And he felt, as deeply as he had ever felt in the pulpit, inspired by a passionate desire to give these few youngsters something adequate to their degree of needing and wanting. The whole

world stretched out beyond Browdley, a world they might and probably would never see; could he not show them an inner world of beauty,
visible to all whose eyes were attuned to it? He thought then, quite
suddenly and with an odd sensation of mind-wandering: These walls
would look better with a few pictures--why not some of those coloured
reproductions of Italian primitives, and so on? It wouldn't cost more
than a few shillings; I daresay I could afford it myself. Still, I shall
have to economise for a time--that trip to London will cost a bit, and
the specialist's fee will probably be stiff-five guineas, maybe, or three
if I plead poverty. Wonder if there is anything really serious the mat-
ter--queer how that pain comes and goes--I hadn't it this afternoon
while I was talking to those children in school, but it came back during
tea. Never mind, stick it out, whatever it is--no sense in whining over
things...

The mere thinking of his throat made it feel dry and parched;
he would have poured out a drink from the carafe had not the water
repelled by its stale, yellowish tinge. And just for a moment there
carne over him the most absurd and ridiculous longing for something
he would never dream of having--a glass of beer. One of those dark
brown frothing tumblers he sometimes saw through the windows of
public-houses--public-houses all warm and brightly lit, with men in
them talking sociably and perhaps playing darts. In his mind, just for
the moment, the picture stood out in vivid contrast to the chill, comfortless room in which he was shortly to begin his address.

He half-smiled at the quaintness of the vision, and then, with a
quick return to reality, nodded and smiled to Mr. and Mrs. Garland,
who had just entered. They were by no means 'young people', and he
did not recollect their ever having attended a Guild meeting before;
still, he was glad enough to see them, though faintly surprised.

Swallowing hard to ease the dryness of his throat, Howat rose
from his chair and began to speak. He began haltingly, unfluently, as
he so often did; those who heard him for only the first minute of any
speech or sermon must certainly have thought him a very poor orator.
It was as if he had, by a tremendous effort, to launch himself into a
world of mind and spirit in which words came of their own accord. He
kept saying: Mozart...Mozart...His face had a peculiar nervous twitch
during those initial struggles; his rugged features looked, for the time,
almost agonised; till, with a suddenness that was sometimes rather
amusing, he was 'off'. He had, beyond doubt, a voice and an enuncia-
tion of great beauty.

Certain of his words and phrases sounded, in his own ears, far
above others, and went on echoing long after he had spoken them.

Was he soaring above their heads, he wondered, momentarily, remembering his daughter's caution? Well no, he thought not; he hoped not; and besides, even if he were, perhaps he could get them to soar with him--above their own heads and his too. If only that sharpness in his throat would disappear; it was absurd, at his age, to be bothered in such a way; he was only forty-three and already seeing specialists and worrying about his health. And suddenly, looking round at the young faces in front of him, he saw them all labelled, as it were, with the inevitable doom of age and death; life was so tragically short, and it seemed in some sense a kind of divine toss-up whether one succeeded or failed in getting anything out of it during the time allowed. How necessary to make the most of youth, to pursue while the pursuit had zest, to apprehend the beauty of the world that lay everywhere around, in sight and sound and feeling...He made a pause in his remarks, wound up his portable gramophone, and played over the Trio in E Major and then the two great Overtures; the music floated past him, dissolving, as it were, into the air of which it was born; he always felt that Mozart was like that, perfectly and enchantingly meaningless except for that one central unanalysable meaning--beauty. 'fever, he said when the records were finished, there had been an angel born upon this earth, that angel was Wolfgang Amadeus Mozart. We might not know a very great deal about the future life, but we must feel--indeed it was almost impossible not to feel--that it was linked up in a marvellous way with the beauty of our own world...Mozart...Raphael the painter...William Blake the poet...And then, with a little mist before his eyes, he was aware that he was making contact, that he was actually and for a second or so putting into the minds of these boys and girls an urge, a longing for something beyond their own immediate surroundings.

He finished in secret triumph. He sat down. He felt drained of power, yet with a tired dreamy feeling of having conquered. Yes, yes, he would get those pictures. Was the fog worse, he wondered? His throat was not so bad now, and anyway, he didn't care--he was too tired and triumphant to care. The tune of the E Major Trio was in his ears. What happened next? Oh yes, someone usually got up and moved a vote of thanks. Only a formality--wouldn't take more than a couple of minutes. Then a little chat with anybody who chose to stay behind, then the short walk through the fog across the playground and past the front of the chapel, and so into his house. A cup of hot cocoa. Bed. Heavens--he was tired--he was sure he would sleep well.

Suddenly he realised that Garland was on his feet and beginning to talk. Pity it couldn't have been somebody else; Garland had such a raucous voice and would go on far too long. Never mind, though--decent of him to come.

Garland, in fact, was one of those fussy, self-important men, full of official correctness, who never miss a chance to say 'a few words'. An air of portentous solemnity hovered over everything he did and had, from the pompous modulations of his ill-pronounced words to the black cut-away coat whose collar was always lightly powdered with dandruff. He was rather squat in build, and had a black curling moustache whose waxed ends were absurdly visible when one saw him from the rear. Howat respected him as a trustworthy chapel official, but they had never attempted any more intimate relationship.

Mrs. Garland was a thin-lipped precise-looking woman with a rigidity of bearing less solemn but more aggressive than her husband's.

Garland was saying: "Of course we're all extremely grateful to Mr. Freemantle for his address, but I do feel there is an aspect--and a very important aspect--of his subject which he has left quite out of account. And that is religion. All this talk about beauty--music, poetry, and all that--isn't any use without the true spirit of religion. And I must say I don't hold with him when he said that we might not know a great deal about the future life. I contend, as every true believer must, that we do know a great deal about it--we know all about Heaven, and anyone who doesn't has only got to read his Bible. Fact of the matter is, people don't read their Bibles enough nowadays--there's far too much discussion of other books, poetry, music, and what not. First things should come first...And now let's refresh ourselves with a hymn--'There is a Book who runs may read'..."

Howat's chin and mouth were half-hidden in the palm of his hand. At the mention of the hymn, however, he looked up abruptly and gave the opening note with his clear, vibrant baritone. In a scattered and rather ineffectual way the audience began to sing, led by Howat, and with Garland supplying a morose and untuneful rumble far below any classifiable key. It was unusual to sing hymns after a Guild meeting, but Howat didn't care--Garland could go through the whole hymnbook if he wanted. Howat felt: He means well, but I'm glad he doesn't come to these affairs oftener.

The hymn came to an end, and as the audience began to pick up hats and wraps and prepare to disperse, he realised that Garland was waiting behind deliberately, as if he wanted to say something. Howat was just slightly peeved about that; if the fellow wanted to see him, why didn't he call at the Manse? After meetings Howat liked a chat with the youngsters, but there wouldn't be any, clearly, if Garland stayed.

CHAPTER ONE - MONDAY

After a few moments he was quite alone in the room with Garland and Mrs. Garland. The others had all disappeared through the green-baize door, and there was left no sound except the hissing of the four gas jets. Howat remarked conversationally as he packed up his gramophone: "Bad night, Mr. Garland." (Garland was the sort of man who wouldn't do for anyone to drop the prefix.)

"Very," replied Garland, massively, and went on: "As a matter of fact, Mr. Freemantle, we shouldn't have come but, only we thought it would give us a chance of seeing you in private."

"Really? Well, anything I can do, of course--" He felt so thoroughly tired, and more in the mood for anything on earth than for a private talk with Garland. However...

"You see, Mr. Freemantle, it's about our girl. She's run away from. home."

"Indeed?" he made the necessary mental effort--Garland's daughter--the girl he had been teaching German--a pleasant girl, she had always seemed, and she had surprised him once, he recollected, by humming a tune from a Brahms sonata.

He repeated: "Indeed? She's run away from home, you say?"

"Yes. On Saturday. She packed up all her things and went before we knew anything about it."

"But surely--"

"Oh, it astonishes you, does it?" interrupted Mrs. Garland, tartly. "We thought maybe you mightn't be so astonished as we were, seeing the chances she's had lately of confiding in you."

"Confiding in me?" Howat was sheerly bewildered. "I don't understand you, Mrs. Garland--I really don't understand. Your daughter has been taking lessons in German from me week by week, but apart from that--"

"And it wasn't our idea she should do it, please don't think that for a moment. What would she be wanting to learn German for, I should like to know?"

"She gave no definite reason--not to me, anyhow--but I suppose she wished to improve her general education. Surely there's nothing very outrageous in that."

"It's all very outrageous. She was full of mad ideas, always was."

"But in these days, Mrs. Garland--"

"*These days*? It's a pity these days are what they are. A sinful, godless age, that's what it is."

Howat's fingers drummed on the desk-lid; he was becoming just a shade impatient. "Well, well, that's a big subject--you were telling me about your daughter, weren't you? Do you mean that she's disappeared, and that you don't know where she is at all?"

Garland here thought fit to intervene; he said, as if realising that his wife would only bungle the business: "The fact is, Mr. Freemantle, we can only guess. We've had no news at all except a card saying she was quite well but wouldn't be coming back. We couldn't read the postmark. And what crossed our minds was that perhaps she might have hinted to you something about her intentions. It's a most upsetting thing to have happened altogether."

"I agree with you, Mr. Garland, and I wish I could help, but I assure you she never gave me the slightest idea that such a notion was in her mind. If she had, I need hardly say that I should have strongly dissuaded her and even, if necessary, approached you on the matter."

Garland seemed to find this reply moderately satisfactory, but Mrs. Garland's eyes narrowed sharply. "You mean that you haven't heard from her at all, then?" she interposed.

He shook his head and then suddenly remembered the Raphael picture that had arrived by the first post that day. "Stay, though--well yes, now I come to recollect it, I did hear from her this morning, but it was merely a short message to say she wouldn't be coming for her usual German lesson to-morrow."

"Oh? So she has written to you then? Was that all she said? Did she give no explanation?"

"She merely said she would be out of Browdley at the time."

"What was the postmark?"

"I must confess I didn't notice."

"Perhaps you still have the letter and it could be examined."

"I don't know, I'm afraid. It may be torn up--quite probably it is. Naturally it didn't strike me as particularly important when I received it."

Garland again took the lead. "Well, Mr. Freemantle, it's an unfortunate business, anyhow. She's left home, and we don't know what's happening to her."

Howat found himself slowly rising out of a dream into this new and intricate reality that was being forced upon him. "But surely, Mr. Garland, you have some idea *why* she's gone, at any rate? That seems to me almost as important as where she is, apart from the fact that it might afford a clue. She can't have acted like that without some big reason of her own."

He felt: Why are they bothering me about it? I can't help them, but I can see now it was a mistake to give the girl German lessons--I never guessed that her parents didn't approve of it. She ought to have told me, really...

"Oh, she has her reasons, I've no doubt," retorted Mrs. Garland, sourly. "And precious fine reasons they are, too, if they were only known, I daresay. The idea--talking of giving up her job at the library and going abroad! That's what she did talk about, though you mayn't believe it. Of course we forbade it--absolutely. A good deal that we don't like we may have to put up with in these days, but there are certain limits, I'm glad to say.

"She talked of going abroad, did she?"

"She's been talking of it off and on for some time. But it came to a head last Friday night when we found she'd been writing to a travel agency about railway tickets to Paris. And then, if you please, she calmly told us that she was going to go abroad in any case."

"To Paris?"

"That's one of the things we have to guess. It doesn't sound a nice sort of place for a young girl to want to go to, does it?"

"But, really, she must have had some purpose in mind? People don't suddenly go to Paris without any reason at all. Did she give you no idea how--how she intended to support herself while she was away?"

Mr. Garland rubbed his nose decisively. "We didn't argue with her, Mr. Freemantle. When a daughter calmly informs her parents that she's going to do what they've forbidden her to do, there's nothing left to argue about. She went up to her bedroom--as we hoped, to think it over and come to her senses. It seems, though, that she just packed her things, went to bed, and went off early in the morning by the first train before any of us was up. Altogether a most disgraceful affair. Of course one naturally thinks of all sorts of possibilities when a girl does a thing like that."

Howat stared far away over Garland's head. "I must say, from a very slight acquaintance with your daughter, she didn't really seem to me the sort of girl who would do anything that either you or she would need to be ashamed of."

"That remains to be found out," answered Mrs. Garland. "And I don't mind telling you to your face, Mr. Freemantle, I think you're one of the prime causes of it all! You have a thoroughly unsettling in-fluence on the young people--you always have had--you put ideas into their heads--it was quite enough to listen to you to-night to realise how all these things begin. As my husband said, there's a great deal too much loose talk in the world nowadays, and ministers, of all people, ought to know better than join in it. They're here to give us religion, that's what I say, not the things of this world."

Howat said, rather curtly: "I don't think we can discuss all that. You must let me know if there's anything practical I can do. And I'm afraid I must go now. Good-night, Mrs. Garland. Goodnight, Mr. Garland." There was something unusual and rather sharp in his eyes.

He strode out of the schoolroom into the cold moist fog. Something was hammering away in his head--a sort of desperately controlled temper, something that made him feel hot and ice-cold simultaneously. Those intolerable people! He could not bring himself to hate them, but his impatience of them was like a flame. And then quite suddenly the flame died down and he felt merely tired, emptied of all energy and willpower and enthusiasm. He found his way into the dark house and, over the remains of the kitchen fire, made himself a cup of cocoa. It was after midnight when he got to bed, and though his tiredness had increased with every moment, he did not find it easy to sleep.

CHAPTER TWO - TUESDAY

The next morning, Tuesday, there was no fog or rain, but a clear frosty sunlight and a high wind from the east that scoured the streets of Browdley till they looked like bones picked clean. Most of Howat's morning study hours were taken up by callers, and at eleven he went out with the intention, before anything else, of getting his first breath of fresh air for several days.

Once the pedestrian leaves the outskirts of Browdley he enters a flat, loamy, and not unpicturesque countryside, studded with small farms and semi-industrialised villages, with here and there a barn or an old mill that Rembrandt might have etched. There are paths through almost every field and in all directions, but one cannot, during an ordinary walk, lose sight of Browdley. Indeed, Browdley looks almost more massive and dominating at a distance of a few miles than closer by. Its factories huddle together into a compact pile, and on a misty day the observer might with a little effort fancy himself in sight of some medieval walled and fortified city, so sharply do the square cliff like factories mark the outlines of the place. There are dozens of tall chimney-stacks, but at such a moment they can seem almost decorative--the spires, perhaps, of the black cathedrals of industrialism.

On Tuesday morning Howat took his favourite walk, which was along School Lane for a quarter of a mile beyond the town, across the potato fields to Shandly's Farm, and then back over the railway and along the bank of the canal. The sun was shining, and he walked fast, enjoying the cold wind and the cheerful landscape. Those who saw him doubtless envied a parson's freedom to take a constitutional on a fine morning.

Mentally, however, he was still ruffled from that talk with the Garlands the previous evening, and as often happened, his mood was inclined to be one of rather desperate unbelief in himself. After all, *could* he be quite sure that what he was doing in Browdley was for the best? Could he even be quite sure that he was doing any good in Browdley at all? Mrs. Garland had accused him of unsettling the young, of putting ideas into their heads--well, all that, in a way, was what he wanted to do; and yet, when the balance was struck, was the net result indubitably favourable? He wished there were someone over him to say, with authority, either Yes, go ahead, you're all right', or

No, stop it at once, you're wrong'. That was the weakness, he had always felt, with these independent Nonconformist creeds--a man, if he were sincere, had to work everything out for himself, and by the time he had finished doing that he had often worried himself into complete lack of confidence in his own judgment.

Of course, so far as the runaway daughter herself was concerned, he was fairly certain he had not been to blame. She had rarely attended chapel, and had not been a member of any of its associated societies; his influence on her, of whatever kind, could only have been slight. There had been the German lessons, true, but they had always, he recollected, been strictly matter-of-fact; indeed, it was curious how little he knew about the girl after those regular weekly meetings--she had told him practically nothing about herself, and he, perhaps unconsciously, had found this a welcome change from the usual outpourings of self-revelation to which every parson becomes accustomed. Apart from those German lessons, and a few chance words in the library where she worked, he hardly remembered ever speaking to her at all. And that reminded him, as he turned homeward along the canal bank, that he might use the remaining time before dinner to change a few library books for young Trevis.

It was a relief, after so much doubting and self-incredulity, to be of some plain and obvious service to somebody. Trevis was a young fellow of twenty-one, who, after a successful and even brilliant career at Cambridge, had had a bad motorcycling smash and was compelled for the present to take a complete rest. The injuries had affected his spine, and Ringwood as well as more exalted medical authorities were not too optimistic about recovery. Fortunately old Mr. Trevis was fairly well off and could afford to keep the boy at home but the latter hated Browdley with a fierceness of which only Howat and Ringwood, perhaps, were aware; it was maddening, on the very brink of what had promised to be a fine career, to have to spend day after day in a stuffy little drawing-room full of presentation silver and unreadable lawbooks. For Mr. Trevis was a solicitor, a prominent local Freemason, and one of the most popular men in the town. Bluff, cheery, happy in his widowerhood, and with an elder son to take over the practice eventually, he did not worry alarmingly about the lad who, apart from a certain stiffness in moving about, did not appear to have very much wrong with him. "What you want is fresh air and exercise," he often said; he did not realise that the boy could not have walked a hundred yards without falling down.

Howat had liked the boy at their first meeting (Ringwood had brought them together--neither Trevis nor his family had ever had any

37

connection with the chapel); and had soon come to feel for him an affection deeper than for anyone he knew outside his own home circle. One of the few ways he could help besides visiting was this changing of library books; he knew the kind of stuff that Trevis liked and took a keen pleasure in making selections which he thought would please. This morning he chose Somerset Maugham's "Moon and Sixpence", Edith Wharton's "Ethan Frome", and a book by a youth named Michael Terry detailing his adventures whilst driving a Ford car across the Northern Territory of Australia from Queensland to the Indian Ocean. Carrying this oddly assorted literature under his arm, Howat called at the house in Mansion Street, and thoroughly enjoyed a half-hour's chat. There was something almost radiantly attractive about the boy now; his earlier robust good looks had been transmuted into a more remote and poignant charm; and to Howat, always acutely eager to put himself into another's position, it seemed as though Trevis must look on life as a receding pin-point of light glimpsed from the interior of a darkening tunnel. He talked to him for a little time about books; it was what they generally talked about; they certainly did not discuss religion. That was a topic Howat would never have been the first to broach. Ringwood, he was aware, told the boy improper stories, and though Howat hoped to satisfy a loftier need, he could never be quite sure that any gift, in such a case, could be more precious than a moment of any sort of amusement.

After they had chatted desultorily for a time, Trevis asked if Howat had chanced to notice Miss Garland on duty at the library. Howat said no, she hadn't been there, and asked why Trevis had enquired. The boy replied: "Because there's a definite rumour going about the town that she's run away with a man."

"With a man, eh?" Howat exclaimed, and in such a tone that Trevis interposed acutely: "Oh, so you did know that she'd run off, then?"

Howat's forehead contracted into a slow frown. "Well, yes, I had heard so. But I didn't know that there was any suggestion of a man in the case."

"Perhaps it isn't true. It's just the sort of thing people in this town would say, anyhow. Did you know her at all, by the way? Her father's something to do with your church, isn't he?"

"Yes, he's the chapel secretary. But I don't know the girl at all well, though it so happens that for the last few months I've been giving her private lessons in German."

"Oh, indeed? Enterprising idea. How did you like her?"

"Like her? Well, she seemed a pleasant sort of girl, though I can't say I formed any definite opinion. I just taught her the German, that was all--we never talked on any other matters."

"That's just like you, isn't it?" Trevis laughed. "I can see now why you've got the reputation in this town of being absolutely impervious to female charm. I don't suppose you even noticed whether the girl was pretty or not?"

Howat smiled; it slightly gratified him to receive this kind of unsolicited testimonial, for it had always been his aim to avoid any of that foolishness that so often mars and complicates the relationship between a minister and the younger ladies of his congregation. He replied: "Well, anyhow, I certainly don't recollect that she *was* pretty."

"She isn't," Trevis said, abruptly. "But she's attractive, in her own way."

"You know her, then?"

"I used to. I haven't seen much of her for the last few years, though--I've been away so often, and she also doesn't spend more time in. Browdley than she needs. They say that most nights she's off to Manchester as soon as the library closes down, and that she doesn't come back till the last train. Gay life, eh? Possibly--I should say she's capable of most things, and certainly of not telling anyone her own business. Unusual sort of girl."

"And you used to know her well?"

"Yes, till my old man quarrelled with her old man-that must have been about ten years ago. Dad was old Garland's solicitor, you know, and solicitors have pretty cast-iron consciences, but even Dad boggled at some of Garland's business. Anyhow, they had a fine old row which ended by Garland taking his affairs somewhere else. I remember it all quite well--the girl and I were of the age when we were told that we mustn't play with each other any more."

"And you didn't?"

"Oh, yes, we did, lots of times. But we gradually saw less of each other, for all that. I always rather liked her, I must say, and I'd be sorry if she'd made a fool of herself. I suppose it doesn't exactly fall within your province to do anything in the matter?"

"At present the difficulty is that she hasn't let anyone know where she's gone to. Of course, if I could do anything I would--very willingly."

"Yes, I'm sure," said Trevis, and the matter dropped.

During dinner at the Manse conversation eddied and swirled around the dramatic disappearance of Elizabeth Garland, and Howat, in the centre of the whirlpool, was rather baffled by it all. He knew so little, and both his wife and Aunt Viney seemed to expect him to know so much; there were, it appeared, all kinds of astonishing rumours about the town. Not only was it now definitely accepted that the girl had absconded with a man, but the man himself had been provisionally identified as a member of a cinema orchestra in Manchester. It was quite obvious, Mrs. Freemantle said, that the girl had a completely bad character, and everyone must feel sympathy for Mr. and Mrs. Garland, such respectable people, in having been so disgraced. "And to think," commented Aunt Viney, "that only last Tuesday she was here for her German lesson, as large as life!"

"I wonder," continued Mrs. Freemantle, "that you found it possible to get on at all with her, Howat. But then you're so unobservant about things. I must say, *I* never took to her."

Howat said nothing for the simple reason that there seemed to him nothing to say; he had already heard quite enough talk about the girl, besides which, he hated gossip, especially of the less charitable kind.

"And as for sending you that picture of a woman, I consider it nothing less than shameless in the circumstances," Mrs. Freemantle still went on. (Aunt Viney must have told her about it, Howat reflected; but then, of course, Aunt Viney always did tell her about everything.) "She must actually have posted it on Saturday, when she was on her way with that man. I'm surprised, Howat--I really am surprised that even you could have gone on giving her those lessons week after week without noticing anything!"

Howat crumbled his bread uncomfortably. "But, my dear, what *could* I have noticed? I merely taught her German. She behaved quite' normally while she was here, if that's what you mean. And I do think that it would be better to refrain from judging the matter until--at any rate--we know a little more about it."

And with this very mild rebuke, which he did not for a moment expect to have any effect, he relapsed again into silence.

During the afternoon he 'visited'. He believed that it was no use preaching at people merely; you must go and see them in their own homes and get to know them personally. He had always been regular and conscientious in so doing, but he did not, despite that, reckon himself a good 'visitor'. He was pretty fair with people who were in any trouble or who needed the more straightforward kinds of advice, and he was all right with people who happened to attract him personally, and he was always a huge success with children; but there were a few persons who came into none of these categories. He was never quite certain whether they dreaded meeting him as much as he dreaded meeting them; and for the sake of this meagre doubt he kept up the practice, till, after several years of it, he had developed a barely adequate technique of small-talk suitable for such occasions.

This afternoon he did a rather strange thing; he thought of all the people he least liked to visit, and visited them one after another. He did not quite know why he did this--not entirely, anyhow, to mortify the spirit, and certainly not at all with any idea of 'getting them over'. On the contrary these visits were to be extra ones--surplus dividends, as it were, from the store of loving kindness in his heart. He thought: If I'm going to be any good in this town, I've got to dive far deeper than I've done hitherto. Yesterday, while I was with Miss Monks, my feelings were absolutely selfish--I was thinking all the time what an old tyrant she was and wondering how soon I could decently get away-- that, remember, with one of my chapel-members lying on her deathbed. After all, what do I do in this town with any enthusiasm except the things I like doing?--I like pottering about with children and young people, I like giving talks on literature and music, I like preaching, too, in a way--I like all these things, and therefore I do them. It all boils down to the fact of a rather stupendous selfishness masquerading as virtue; the truth is, I'm no better than anyone else--I like what I like. But as a parson I ought to be different--yes, better--or else, in Heaven's name, why do I wear this collar the wrong way round?

So, in a state of self-disgust that only gradually wore itself out, he visited old Jack Harmon, who was nearly stone deaf and was interested in nothing but Association football. Not only had he to be shouted at in a way of which his daughters alone had acquired the perfect knack, but his voice, when he spoke, was a barely coherent muttering to which nobody in his house ever paid the slightest attention. Howat, moreover, was not learned in football, and could only vaguely follow the gist of the man's talk. The pleasure his visit was giving was, however, obvious--too obvious, perhaps, since the old man, delighted to entertain the parson in a room which directly overlooked the street and through whose window every passer-by could see, clucked and gurgled his satisfaction till the saliva dribbled inelegantly down his chin. Howat shouted "Yes" and "No" and "Really?" while the pain in his throat, rarely absent altogether, became a white-hot ache; then, after about an hour, he managed to drag himself away, pursued even from the street-door by the man's joyful incoherencies.

Next he called on Mrs. Roseway in Hill Grove (he had intended visiting her the previous day, but had put it off with an excuse which, he knew now, had been merely a disguise for selfish personal reluctance); she was eighty-four, and did nothing but grumble because she had rheumatism ("By Jove," Ringwood had once said, "it's time she had something!") Howat had never been able to make any headway against the quiet, almost contented querulousness of this old creature; she was fairly well off, yet (again quoting Ringwood) 'you couldn't get a penny out of her without chloroform'. She had children, hard-working but unfortunate, living in neighbouring towns, and Howat always hoped he might some day persuade her to deal more generously with them. He had often come near to the point of broaching the matter, but had never quite managed it; this afternoon, with new determination in his heart, he decided that he would. He listened for a time to her complaints, and then began a plea for greater charitableness and help towards those in need of it, till at last the old lady, shrewdly perceiving where his eloquence might lead, shut him up with a quite final if not very courteous remark and resumed the more satisfying topic of her own ailments.

Then he visited Joe Maracot, a former chapel member, now turned atheist, who had fallen off a lorry and fractured a leg. Maracot treated him with scarcely veiled hostility; he was a strong Labour enthusiast, an admirer of Councillor Higgs, and tried to lure Howat into an argument about Russia, but Howat, feeling himself being baited, declined to be drawn.

Then (purely as a treat for himself) he looked in at the Infirmary and spent half an hour in the children's ward. After that he called on the two Miss Jekylls, who talked endlessly about foreign missions--a department of religious enterprise for which he had never, somehow, been able to share the optimism of its partisans. The continual twitter of the two ladies bored him (try as he would he could not help it), and their vision of an Africa perfected by frock-coats and hymn-books had that large simplicity that always affected him with a certain sadness of mind. And yet, he felt, the Misses Jekyll were very likeable; they believed in their vision and subscribed money for it with far more generosity than they could really afford (there was a little box for 'missionary pennies' behind the clock on the mantelpiece); they thought as kindly of an idealised black man bowing down to wood and stone as they did harshly of the real unfortunates who lived within a quarter-mile of their own house. If only Howat could give a twist to that pathetic stream of good will, could bring it nearer home and canalise it so that it ran in a warming current through the streets of Browdley! He tried valiantly, but as fast as he mentioned local hardship, the two ladies romped merrily along to some other instance of wholesale conversion in distant lands--"over a thousand baptised last month in India alone, so my missionary cousin writes to me." Howat forebore to reply that during that same month in India there must have been at least a quarter of a million non-Christians born; he felt so sure that they would be offended as well as unable to see the point of such a remark. He just let them talk on, accepted a cup of tea and a piece of cake, and then, after many mutual assurances that the visit had been enjoyable, took his leave.

Lastly he visited an old man, a former chapel caretaker, slowly dying of heart disease; the man was obviously too ill to talk or to want to be talked to, and Howat did not stay more than a few minutes.

By that time it was time for 'high tea' at the Manse.

After tea he went into his study and prayed. He did not kneel or even bow his head; he just sat back in an armchair before the fire and shut his eyes. He did not want his wife or Aunt Viney to come in (as they would often do without knocking) and find him in an obviously prayerful attitude; not that he was ashamed of praying, but prayer to them was such a professional business, something a parson did night and morning, a good deal on Sunday, and occasionally at other people's bedsides; he was sure they would think him ill if they caught him at it on any less customary occasion. Besides, his wasn't a definite prayer; he didn't put much of it even into words; it was just an expression of the feeling of worthlessness that had come over him, the doubt as to whether he was doing any good, and the desire to be given (if it were possible) some secret reassurance.

As it chanced, Aunt Viney did interrupt; a message, she said, had come from Miss Monks--would Howat call round and see her some time that evening, if he could, as it was important?

He sighed and answered yes, certainly. It was all over the town, of course, that the old woman was dying, and that Ringwood had given her the news, however, had been dwarfed in significance by that more exciting business about Garland's daughter. He put on his hat and overcoat and went into the chilly, lamp-lit streets. Well, he reflected, he would have a chance to do better with the poor old soul than the day before--perhaps it was more than he deserved. But he was very tired again, and there was the Temperance meeting he ought to look in at later on--they liked him to lead the singing.

He reached the house in Lower George Street about half-past seven, and was shown up into that same stuffy, stale-smelling bedroom. But instead of a dying woman's greeting he was welcomed by a brisk "Good evening, Mr. Freemantle ", and saw Miss Monks sitting up cheerfully in bed with her eyes fixed on him in a way that put him rather in mind of a snake poised to strike. He began:

"Well, Miss Monks, and how are you to-day?" in the usual manner, but he was hardly prepared for the tremendous precision with which she replied: "Better."

"Better? That's great--great!" he murmured, and added irrelevantly that it was a gloriously clear evening, cold, but no fog--so different from yesterday.

"And so I suppose," said Miss Monks, ignoring the weather, "that Garland's girl has run away from home?"

"I believe so, yes."

"I'm not surprised. There was always something queer about that girl. I put it all down to not being made to go to chapel--Garland seemed to have no control over her at all. And then having that job at the library, too." She paused and continued impressively: "There are books in that library, Mr. Freemantle, whether you believe me or not, which ought not to exist anywhere--let alone where young people can get hold of them. I don't hold with public libraries."

Howat made no answer to that, but smiled gently and waited for her to get to the real reason why she had sent for him. It was soon forthcoming. It appeared that she had been on the point of death about three o'clock that morning and had then made a sudden recovery. She was convinced it was a miracle--the special intervention of a Providence evidently desirous of preserving her for some future activity. "I'm grateful, too, for such mercies," she added, "and I'd like you, Mr. Freemantle, to join with me in a little prayer of thankfulness."

So he prayed again, and when that was over she went on to say that, as a more practical expression of gratitude, she had been thinking of making an alteration in her will. She had only a few hundred pounds to dispose of, and as the will stood, it was all left to Mrs. Kerfoot, her widowed niece who lived next door and had looked after her for many years. In view, however, of the recent dramatic intervention of Providence, she had come to feel that this would be a selfish arrangement; a hundred pounds would surely be enough for Mrs. Kerfoot, and the rest could then be devoted to loftier things. She had been thinking out details, in fact, ever since early morning, and had already sent a message to her lawyer. What she had in mind was some sort of charity, associated with the chapel and administered by the parson. She knew there were several existing charities of the kind in Browdley--one provided for loaves and candles to be given every Christmas to fifty deserving Church of England spinsters--she had often seen mentions of it in the local paper, and she had noticed that it was always called after the name of the original benefactor. Something like that she had in mind; it seemed to her a really charitable way of disposing of money, much better than leaving it all in bulk to a private person, however deserving.

Howat listened rather unhappily as she expounded this evidently well-prepared scheme. He mentioned with diffidence that most charities of such a kind dated from hundreds of years back, when social conditions were different, and survived nowadays merely as antiquities. He also indicated that it was already becoming a matter of some intricacy to discover the fifty deserving spinsters who would accept the Christmas loaves and candles, and that the vicar of the parish church had often commented that there ought to be some way of altering things to fit in with more modern needs. In his (Howat's) opinion, if she would forgive him for expressing it, he didn't think such a bequest would really be the best way of using the money; there were many other things in these days--the infirmary, for instance, which badly required new X-ray equipment, or the cottage hospital--

But that, if he had remembered, was tactless of him, for Miss Monks had a violent grudge against all such institutions, and answered tartly: "Not with *my* money, thank you, Mr. Freemantle--I don't hold with them at all. Those who give to such things can do what they like with their own, but I have a right to do what I like with mine."

"Oh quite, quite," agreed Howat.

In the end he did, after much persuasion, manage to convince her that a Letitia Monks Bequest on the lines of the loaves and candles would be a rather pointless affair. But he could not convert her to any alternative idea of his own; two things, he realised, were fixed in her mind--first, that the bequest should be connected with the chapel, and second, that it should be permanently associated with her own name. Finally, as the only terms on which she could be diverted from something absolutely fatuous, he agreed that the chapel was in some need of a new vestry. Yes, of course, it could be the Letitia Monks Vestry, and the name could be inscribed in stone somewhere--oh yes, he was sure it could. And he would certainly consult with her lawyer about it, if she wished--yes, he would do anything she asked. A splendid idea--extremely generous of her--future generations would undoubtedly appreciate it--oh yes, yes--undoubtedly...

"You see," said Miss Monks, with shrewd triumph, "I feel it's the chapel that has made me what I am."

He stayed a little longer till a distant chiming reminded him that it was nine o'clock; he had been there for an hour and a half; it really was time he looked in at that Temperance meeting. He was just shaking hands and preparing to leave when Ringwood's brusque voice came booming up the stairs.

CHAPTER TWO - TUESDAY

Ringwood, red-cheeked and cheerful as ever, came striding
into the room in his heavy motoring coat. "Hullo, Miss Monks!
Thought I'd just look in to see you again on my way home! Still feeling better? That's right--take things easily. Hullo, Freemantle--you
here, too? Wonderful old lady, isn't she? No, don't run away--we'll go
down together in a minute just give me time to hold her hand!"

He had an air with him, Ringwood had; and Howat had often
half-envied it. He was bluff and sometimes rude in his jovial way, but
nobody ever minded--not that he cared if they did. He was by far the
most popular doctor in Browdley; he was generous, kind-hearted, and
hard-working, but he stood no nonsense and never let anyone waste
his time. And the brusquer he was, the more, in a way, he was liked. In
a few years, when his hair had turned completely white, he and his
sayings would doubtless begin to grow legendary.

Miss Monks, at eighty-nine, was no more impervious to that
forceful charm than many a girl in her teens. She simpered almost
coyly as Ringwood felt her pulse and passed a hand across her forehead. "Keep quiet," he adjured her. "You've been talking too much.
Freemantle's fault, I daresay. Good night, now. Sleep well. And I'll be
round in the morning."

He nodded, drew on his gloves, and took Howat's arm; and the
latter, with a murmured farewell to the old lady, allowed himself to be
piloted downstairs and into the street. The doctor's Morris, five years
old, waited at the kerb. "Get inside," said Ringwood, "I'm going to
drive you home."

Howat clambered in; he was weary, and not sorry to be given
a lift. "It's a cold night," he commented. "Damn cold," agreed Ringwood, and slipped into gear. It was difficult to talk during the drive, as
the car made at least twice as much noise as any other Howat had ever
experienced; he stared ahead through the murky windscreen, a little
confused in mind with that sudden rush of lamp-posts and shop-fronts
past him. "That was a stuffy room," he shouted, as if in indirect explanation of his silence. Ringwood shouted back: "Sour as a midden.
Why don't she have a window opened? How long had you been
there?" Howat answered: "Since about half-past seven," and Ringwood, with a curious and characteristic noise in his throat, exclaimed:
"Good God!"

Then it was gradually borne upon Howat's mind that Ringwood was driving him, not to the Manse, but to his own house in
Dawson Street. He said "I say, Ringwood, I thought you were taking
me home," and Ringwood replied, gruffly: "So I am--to *my* home.
What more do you want?" Howat began to explain his Temperance

meeting, but Ringwood interrupted: "My dear man, you're coming in with me for a while, and your temperance people can all go and drink themselves to death."

They drew up outside the ugly detached villa in which the doctor lived. He had only a housekeeper to look after him, and the house was many rooms too big; it had formerly belonged to an older-fashioned doctor with a large family, a top-hat and tail-coat, and a brougham. Ringwood had made no effort to adapt the premises to his more modest uses; some of the rooms were altogether unfurnished, and all were shabby. He had a decent income, but he never cared about the more complicated comforts of life; he would keep the chairs in his dining-room till they actually fell to pieces, just as he would drive his old car till the repairers finally declined to patch it up any more. He liked good, plain food and fifteen-year-old whisky, and (when he had any spare time, which was not often) he would read any sort of book except novels.

"Go on," he said, almost pushing Howat out of the car. He followed the parson up the short gravelled path and, unlocking a side-door, manoeuvred him into the unlit waiting-room that adjoined the surgery. "Straight through--you know the way," he directed, switching on a light. The unlovely room faced them with its stiff array of straight-backed chairs and table of ancient magazines. Ringwood passed through into the surgery beyond. It was a crowded, glass-roofed apartment, not unlike a greenhouse, full of the usual smell of drugs and india-rubber, and lined with shelves of books, bottles, and the accumulated litter of three decades in Browdley. It was extraordinary, though true, that amidst this confusion Ringwood always did know exactly where everything was.

"Now," said the doctor, "sit down and make yourself comfortable."

He put Howat in a big leather chair that could be made to tilt backwards--the chair in which, before the days of specialised dentistry, many a Browdley sufferer had lost an aching tooth. Then he lit the gas-fire and wandered away into the small dispensary that opened off the surgery at the further end. He kept shouting out from this inner room, his words punctuated with the clink of bottles and glasses.

"Yes, I was wrong about the old girl after all, Freemantle--you win that bob. Could have sworn she'd peg out during the night--never was more surprised than when I saw her perking up in bed at ten o'clock this morning. They'll have to shoot her, that's all...Seriously, though, her heart's pretty dicky--take her off sudden one of these days.

I wouldn't mind betting all the money I've got that you and I'll be in at the kill before this time next month."

Howat half-smiled; Ringwood's flippant phrases sometimes shocked, but never exactly offended him. He said, after a pause: "You know, Ringwood, I often envy you doctors. There's something so downright about the things you do for people. We parsons have to grope about wondering what we *can* do. You just go and do it. To-night, for instance, you took that woman's pulse and temperature in about a minute--probably a far more useful service than I managed to perform in the whole hour and a half I was there with her."

"Oh, I don't know--it depends a lot on what you did do. Chat-tered, I suppose--I noticed her heart was a bit jerkier after it. If she dies in the night I shall put on the certificate 'Talked to death by a parson.' Can't think what you found to say to her all that time, I must admit."

"Well, for one thing, I prayed." He said that in a queerly trou-bled voice, and added: "Does that sound to you a rather odd confession?"

"Not at all. After all, it's in your line of business, just as I tap chests and look at tongues."

"I wonder if it really is quite the same sort of thing as that."

"Sometimes, Freemantle, I think you wonder a damn sight too much." Ringwood came bounding out of the dispensary with a tumbler of whisky and water in one hand and a half-filled medicine-glass in the other. The latter he held out to Howat. "Here, drink this. You need it-- it's only a pick-me-up--quite harmless and nonalcoholic. Don't think I haven't noticed the state you've been getting yourself into these last few months."

Howat took the glass. "Thanks, Ringwood--though I'm not sure I do need it. Touch of nerves, perhaps. A few rather troublesome things have been happening lately. Last night, for instance, I had a worrying kind of interview with the chapel secretary, Garland."

"Oh, Garland the draper?--yes, I know him. Little chap with black moustaches--looks rather like a seedy croupier at a fifth-rate ca-sino. Well, what was all the fuss over? They say, by the way, his daughter's hopped it--maybe the old boy was feeling a bit peeved over that when you saw him."

"It was about that--that we had the--the argument," said Howat. Then he told Ringwood briefly all the details. Ringwood lis-tened intently, perching himself on the edge of the desk and sipping whisky from time to time. At the end of the story he said: "So they're trying to blame you for what's happened, are they? Well, I don't think I'd worry about it if I were you. Queer sort of girl, I remember--rather nice voice--good figure, too--I had to give her the once-over, you know, before she took on that job at the library. Cut above her pa and ma, I thought jolly good luck to her if she *has* left the old folks at home. Wish there were more would do it--look at the unemployed-- thousands of 'em--no initiative--no ambition--rather hang about Browdley street-corners than try their luck anywhere else. Of course they might say much the same of us--we stick to the old place, don't we?--but then, we're getting on--at least I am--I'm sixty next birthday. But you're not so old, Freemantle--I often wonder why you stay on here. Don't you ever feel you'd like to try for a change?"

"Often. Terribly often. But there again, you doctors have the advantage. You could clear out to-morrow and feel that you were doing just as much good somewhere else, but I couldn't--it's taken me twelve years even to begin to do anything here, and if I went away all that would probably be wasted."

"Oh, nonsense. You parsons take yourselves far too seriously. After all, if you do your best, what more *can* you do? That's how I always feel in my job. Sometimes I cure, sometimes I kill--people take the risk when they call me in--I make no promises except to do as well as I know how. If I come a cropper over something it's not my fault--I can't help it--and I assure you I never let it lose me a wink of sleep. Why should I?"

"I know," Howat said. "But then, you're so certain of the good you do--you know it--you can see it with your own eyes--people whom you've cured walk about the streets as a living reminder and proof."

"And a damn sight worse off some of 'em are than if I'd killed 'em! My dear chap, it isn't a matter of doing good, it's a matter of carrying on with a job. If I once began to think in terms of ethics, I should probably send old mother Roseway an overdose of strychnine to-night- -yes, and a dozen others I could name. Fortunately I'm content to plod along at the job I'm paid for, and it's a pity you can't be satisfied in the same way. After all, you preach, you visit, you bury and marry and all that, you run no end of societies and things--I should imagine you give pretty good value for money, on the whole."

"It isn't even that. I've got to satisfy myself."

Ringwood approached Howat and laid a firm hand on his shoulder. "You know, Freemantle, I should say you were in for a fairly serious breakdown if you don't take care. You want a holiday--some kind of change from this infernal round of visiting old women and singing temperance hymns." His voice, which had been serious for a moment, relapsed into its more usual bantering tone as he added: "Personally I never take holidays of the ordinary kind--haven't done for twenty years--but when I feel myself getting a bit edgy I ring up Hudson and hand him over my practice for two or three days; then I pop off to London and have a real good beano. Dinner at a chophouse, then the silliest show I can find, then a few drinks wherever I can get them, then--well, I wouldn't like to tell you all that is on the programme sometimes when I'm in town. But it doesn't often happen--I find a few days of dissipation lasts me longer now than it used to. Growing old, I suppose that's what it is."

Howat smiled. "I'm sure you can't really see me doing anything of that sort. Though as a matter of fact I do happen to be going to London this Friday--I've got to come to terms with a firm about supplying a new heating apparatus for the chapel."

"Well, there's your chance. You won't be all day choosing a heating apparatus. And I don't expect you'll hurry back to this benighted spot by the very next train, will you?"

"I shall put up for the night at one of those bed-and-breakfast hotels in Southampton Row, and probably catch the 10.30 back on Saturday morning."

"Rubbish, man! Stay in town and make a week-end of it!"

"Perhaps I might except for the fact that I have a Bazaar committee-meeting and a young men's class on Saturday evening and two services to take on Sunday, as well as Sunday school and the Armistice service. People don't realise that a parson has work to do--indeed, I hardly dare mention to most people that I'm going to London; they look at me with that 'lucky dog' expression, as if I were just treating myself to a holiday."

"Which is precisely what you ought to be doing. Anyhow, you'll have one night in town--and take my tip: make a real night of it--dinner and theatre--don't stint yourself--don't go to bed till the small hours. Remember that: I shall ask you, mind, when you get back, for a full report, and if you haven't taken my prescription there'll be trouble!"

They laughed and chatted on for a few minutes longer, until Howat looked at his watch and said he must be going. He rose and glanced shyly at Ringwood, for momentarily he had an impulse to tell the doctor about that pain in his throat. Why not, after all?--it would save a few guineas, and if it were anything serious...but the mere possibility checked the words long before they could have reached his lips. Ringwood had been a good friend for years, and Howat suspected real affection behind the ferocity of manner; it would all be so much less unnerving with someone whom he did not know.

AND NOW GOODBYE

He said good-bye, but Ringwood insisted on driving him back to the Manse. When at last he was alone in his study, glancing at a few things that had arrived by the evening post, he began to think in some detail about his Friday plans. He would travel up by a morning train, arriving in London soon after lunch; he could see the engineering people in the early afternoon, and then be at Wimpole Street for four. And after that? It would depend, of course, on how he felt; he might not be in the mood for anything at all. A pity, perhaps, that he couldn't get back to Browdley the same night...He tore open the wrapper of the London *Times*, which was sent him by post each day, and on the front page an announcement caught his eye--a violin and piano recital at the Cavendish Hall on Friday evening; a good programme, too-- Schumann, Beethoven, Brahms. Sometimes, in earlier years and at very rare intervals, he had made special trips to London to attend some particular concert or recital; he had not done so lately, for financial reasons, but now the thought of sitting once again in a concert-hall and listening to Brahms (Brahms of all composers) gave him a sudden pricking of anticipation 3 whatever dreadful things were in store for him on Friday, that would at least help to redress the balance. He wondered if they would play the Sonata in A major. The opening theme of the first movement began to pour through his mind in a clear stream; it reminded him of something, of somebody, of somewhere he had once heard it before, and not so very long before--curious, yes--he remembered now--he had heard that 'girl humming it at the beginning of one of those German lessons, and he had been too surprised at the time to make a remark or ask a question. Perhaps, he now reflected, she had picked it up from the cinema musician.

CHAPTER THREE - WEDNESDAY

He slept rather well (it might have been, he guessed, that Ringwood's pick-me-up had contained something to make him do so) and woke up feeling considerably refreshed; then, after breakfast, a rare mood seized him, and for the first time for many months he did not spend his allotted morning hours in the study. Instead he adjourned to the room on the opposite side of the lobby--the parlour, a chilly bay-windowed apartment used only on fairly infrequent occasions, and furnished in a style which future period connoisseurs will perhaps extol as Edwardian. There was a litter of spindly chairs, a large-patterned and highly-coloured Axminster, and a good deal of poor-quality inlaid work and china in cabinets. The only object, however, which lured him to this unrewarding scene at nine o'clock on a November morning was the pianoforte--an upright German instrument, not very good in tone, but on the other hand not nearly as bad as its surroundings might have suggested. On and off since he got out of bed Howat had been thinking of that concert on Friday evening; he had already begun to feel a little excited about it, and excitement had put him in one of his periodic moods for what his wife called 'making up bits of tunes'. She could never see much point in the occupation, for although some of the tunes had occasionally won prizes in competitions, they were never 'printed,' as she said, nor did they seem to her at all attractive when Howat played them over to her. She also disliked the sound of improvising and experimentation on the piano, and complained that even in the bedroom she could hear it, and that it always gave her a headache. Howat, therefore, never devoted himself to his 'tunes while she was in the house, which meant that for years he had had very few opportunities of doing so at all. But this morning, Mrs. Freemantle, contrary to usual habit, had taken breakfast downstairs and had gone out immediately afterwards with Aunt Viney; there was a sale at a dress shop in a neighbouring town, and it was most important that she should arrive in time.

Howat, in that cold and unwelcoming room, was almost childishly happy with his music-paper and pencil. They revealed a part of him that few people ever saw; indeed, he kept it particularly to himself, because (for one reason) he did not wish his congregation to think he still had designs on their hymn-book. Years before, when he had first arrived in Browdley, there had been a tremendous row over that; he had nourished great visions of making the chapel a centre of musical culture (why, he had argued, should that sort of thing be left entirely to the Anglicans and Romans?) and had incautiously let it be known that he did not consider certain old and well-known revivalist hymn-tunes to be musically first-rate. The resulting upheaval, which he had barely managed to live down, had convinced him that his more important work would be sadly hampered if he allowed himself to be sidetracked into the position of a musical Savonarola; so thenceforward he had scrupulously left all questions of hymns and anthems to the organist, a local insurance-agent, whose dream was to play the "Poet and Peasant" overture on a three-manual instrument that had a Vox Humana stop.

It was remarkable how completely Howat had learned that early lesson. Rigid self-discipline over a period of years had given him power to tolerate what the strictly musical part of him must have detested; Sunday after Sunday heard him joining, with that deep baritone of his, in music whose words and tunes matched each other in utter commonplaceness; and whenever the critical temptation arose he could manage to stifle it by thinking of the spirit that ranked beyond the mere letter, and of that deep religious feeling which must be held so much more worthy than any technique of art.

This morning, however, no such distracting thoughts occurred to him, and he yielded himself, for two hours and more, to a task which he found totally absorbing. There was a school concert due to take place about Christmas time, and he usually taught the children some kind of song for the occasion; why not, then, something composed by himself, if it seemed good enough when he had finished it? But the idea, after all, did not strike him till he had been some time at work; it was a mere excuse for going on, not a reason for beginning. The truth was, to put it quite plainly: his wife was out and he felt in the mood.

When he left the Manse, a little later than his usual hour (for he had somewhat lost count of time whilst at the piano) he felt pleased, though far from satisfied, with what he had done. It sent him back, in memory, to those very early years when he had day-dreamed himself the author of some colossal symphony, bowing acknowledgments before a frantic first-night audience at the Queen's Hall. Absurd, of course; he knew more accurately now the true extent of his talent; but it was tempting, and rather fragrant, to recollect those ancient ecstasies. Sing-song homeward walks along the Kentish lanes, with stars overhead and his boyhood friends arm-linked on either side; hours with the piano or violin (he played both instruments passably well); trips to Canterbury, Dover, Maidstone, sometimes even London, to sample the art of some celebrity. One after another, and in completely unchronological order, the great masters had moved into his youthful comprehension--Chopin first, then Beethoven, Bach, Mozart, and Brahms last of all. In those days music had seemed everything to him, but that of course was before the crisis in his early life which, though he did not greatly care for the term, could only be called his 'conversion'. Looking back now over a span of a quarter of a century he had a disappointingly vague recollection of how that had happened; but he could remember perfectly a certain winter's night when he had first heard the Kreutzer Sonata and had walked home afterwards along moonlit and frost-bound roads from the railway station...It was a pity, really, that there was no kind of musical club or society in Browdley; he had often thought of starting one, but he was rather afraid it would take up too much of his time. Besides, nowadays people had gramophones and the wireless...He wondered if Higgs, who had said he was keen on music, would support him in the idea of holding short evening concerts on Sundays after the time of church and chapel services? Of course one had to move warily in things like that; there would probably be opposition from some of the older people, or else they would insist that all the music played on such occasions should be 'sacred' music...as if all good music were not sacred...

Howat, striding along the High Street with these and other reflections in mind, was far too preoccupied to keep his usual keen lookout for people he knew; indeed, he was not even looking where he was going and narrowly escaped collision with a man who was standing in a rather peculiar posture on the pavement. He was about to mutter a vague apology when he caught sight of a pair of very recognisable black moustaches. "Ah, Mr. Garland," he exclaimed, and wondered whether Garland really wanted him to stop or not. For Garland was outside his own shop, scrutinising through the glass a roll of cloth which an assistant was fixing in position. At intervals of a few seconds he shouted directions, ignoring the fact that the assistant could not possibly hear him; but as this had been his method of supervising window-dressing for thirty years or so, he probably did not see any reason to alter it. "Ah, good morning, Mr. Freemantle," he answered, swinging round sharply. He stopped, as if waiting for Howat to make the first move in the conversation, and for a few moments the two men stared at each other with some discomfort, while the assistant behind the plate glass stared at both of them impartially. At last Garland

54

opened with: "You've heard the latest news about my daught pose?"

"Latest news? Have you--have you heard from her the

"No, we've not heard, but we've got to know, and that's been quite enough. Come inside a moment--I don't want to shout these things on the pavement."

Howat followed dubiously, reflecting that there was really no need to shout them at all. The interior of Garland's shop, as they both walked through it to an inner apartment, afflicted him with a spasm of melancholy; it was very dark, and the assistants were pale and sickly-looking youths, whom Garland glared at fiercely as he passed them. In a sort of inner office filled with bills and ledgers and patterns of cloth Garland motioned Howat to a chair, closed the door carefully, and resumed: "She's run away with a man--a man who plays the fiddle in a picture-house."

Howat said: "Yes, I'd heard something to that effect, but I was hoping it could be no more than a rumour."

"A *rumour*? God bless my soul, they were seen together at Manchester getting into the train!" His voice thickened with indignation. "Of course neither my wife nor I could countenance that sort of thing. Not at any price would we take her back now that we know what has happened. She's disgraced our name--the only thing we can do is to try to forget that she's our daughter."

Howat found himself staring at a peculiarly sinister-looking tailor's dummy, armless and legless, that had been flung into a corner of the office amidst a heap of brown paper. He had been propelled so abruptly, as it were, from the world of his own thoughts into this other world of angry fathers and erring daughters and rolls of gents' suitings that he could hardly, for the moment, get his bearings. Then the last few words of Garland's remarks echoed in his mind and brought him up with a jerk. He said, rather sadly: "Don't you think it may be a little too early to reach such a decision, Mr. Garland?"

"Not at all. We're a respectable family--we're not going to make any terms with evil-doing. Out she stays, now that she's gone, and I'd say the same to any of my other children. She need never come back to Browdley thinking she'll be admitted here again."

"Well, well, I suppose if you feel like that about it--"

I *do* feel like that, and my wife would say the same. If thine eye offend thee, pluck it out, so the Good Book says."

"It also, I believe, mentions forgiveness--"

"It says we should forgive our enemies, not our daughters."

Which set Howat reflecting absently that it was, most certainly, much easier to forgive one's enemies than one's friends and relatives--could it be, then, that the more difficult achievement was not seriously expected of us? Garland, however, had clearly not meant so much, and Howat answered, with sudden distaste for the entire argument: "Anyhow, Mr. Garland, there doesn't seem much point in discussing all this till we definitely hear where the girl is and what she's doing. I wish--I do wish sincerely--that I could help you in some way--I assure you I sympathise most deeply--"

"I don't see what anybody *can* do. Personally, I don't expect ever to hear from her again--if she's decided to live that sort of life, she'll know that we won't have anything more to do with her. We don't even want to hear her name mentioned. Henceforward--"

Garland continued in this strain for several minutes longer, and Howat, at the first considerable pause, was glad to make his excuses and get away.

The second post usually arrived at the Manse towards noon, and was placed on the study table to await Howat's return from his morning's visits. That Wednesday morning, when he reached home, there was quite a collection for him to deal with--bills, circulars, appeals--the usual mixture, and then, between two larger envelopes, a small one, addressed in a writing which he faintly recognised, though he could not quite decide where he had seen it before. He opened the envelope and read, from a single sheet of plain paper without any address heading:

"DEAR MR. FREEMANTLE,--YOU will be surprised to hear from me, I am sure, but I am presuming on our slight acquaintance to ask a favour. No doubt by this time you and everyone else in Browdley must know that I have left home, and though I do not regret doing so, I do not want my parents to worry about me unnecessarily. I wish you could assure them that I am perfectly all right and quite happy. I hate leaving as I had to do, but I really do feel that I am too old to be treated as a child. Do you think you could possibly explain that to them? I know it is asking a great deal, but I cannot think of anyone else who could do it. I must thank you, too, for the German lessons which I am sure will prove of use to rue, and I enclose two pounds which I think I owe you for them. I have no permanent address just at present, but for the next few clays anything addressed c/o the Charing Cross post office would reach me. With kindest regards and many thanks, Yours sincerely, ELIZABETH GARLAND."

Howat stared at the letter with a sharp sensation of dismay. This Garland affair seemed to get more and more complicated and to be dragging him, against his will, nearer and nearer to the centre of it. He had always been careful to avoid any sort of private friendship with the younger girls of his chapel--he thought it undesirable for a good many reasons--yet here he was, the confidant, whether he chose to be or not, of a girl who had run away from home and was eloping (to use the politest word) to Paris. It was all rather unfortunate, and he did not quite know what would be the best course to take. If he showed the letter or conveyed the message to Garland, he could imagine the fellow's conclusions. Nor, despite the girl's optimism, did he feel at all equal to explaining to Garland that his daughter was 'too old to be treated as a child'. Really, it was a most difficult situation and he went into dinner feeling sadly perplexed. Almost as soon as he sat down, his wife said: "I suppose you didn't call on the Garlands, Howat? Don't you think you ought to--to express our sympathy?"

He answered: "I met Garland in the street outside his shop and we went in for a little talk. I told him how sorry we were."

"Did he tell you that the person the girl's run off with is a man over fifty--married and with a family?"

"Good heavens, no? Wherever did you hear that?"

Mrs. Freemantle smiled in a satisfied way and exchanged a glance with Aunt Viney; it was so rarely that she could rouse her husband's interest, much less a touch of excitement, in any titbit of local gossip. "Viney heard it from a woman in the baker's shop this morning. It's true, because the woman's son has a job at the same cinema--he's a ticket attendant or something."

"I--I don't know. It sounds so--so incredible. A man of that age and a girl of--how old would she be--nineteen--twenty or so--I suppose?"

"She's twenty-two."

Howat did not answer for a time, and at last he merely remarked, as if to himself: "Oh, then she has a legal right to do as she likes. I didn't quite realise that. But still..." He checked himself, feeling he had already discussed the matter at far too great a length. "It's all most unfortunate," he ended up, "and I do think that the less people talk and spread gossip about it, the better."

Wednesday afternoon was the time for the weekly meeting of his Ladies' Working Party and Sewing Guild, and it was his custom to look in about three o'clock, and take an unwanted cup of tea in a schoolroom that always smelt rather depressingly of old clothes. He did not much care for the job, but it was expected of him; the women liked the few minutes of social contact with the minister; it gave them food for gossip afterwards whether he looked well or ill, whether his clothes were shabby, whether he got on all right with his wife, if it were true that his son in Canada had entirely gone to the bad and never wrote home, and so on.

Howat read in his study till three o'clock that afternoon; then he walked over to the schoolroom. The women greeted him with their usual fussy murmurs of appreciation, but it was noticed immediately by the more observant of them that he did not seem altogether himself--he did not make those customary jovial remarks about the garments they were working at, those time-honoured witticisms which never failed to produce attacks of coyly restrained giggling. On the contrary, he seemed preoccupied, his smiles went over their heads as if directed at another world, and he went on stirring his tea in an absent-minded way long after the two lumps of sugar were most certainly dissolved.

And at a quarter-past three, which was rather earlier than his habit, he bade adieu to the ladies and went out into the glooming streets. He felt he wanted a walk, and left the town by the main road, turning into muddy fields as soon as he could. He walked briskly for a mile or so, and then leaning against a stile, re-read the letter in his pocket amidst the falling twilight. A puzzle, really, to know what to do. She had appealed to him, and despite the impossibility of what she asked, he rather liked the style of the letter--simple, straightforward, neither explaining nor apologising, but merely asking. And no mention of the man in the case. That, he thought, showed a certain delicacy. But a married man with a family...really, how could such a thing be possible?

Howat, in fact, was bewildered; for, despite his years, he knew little about the world of private scandal--certainly less than did an average girl at a boarding-school, He never read the *News of the World*, and never went to the cinema; throughout his adult life, even during the War, he had preserved an ignorance, perhaps even an innocence, that was largely compounded of distaste and lack of interest. Divorces, liaisons, *crimes passionels*, and all the rest of the Sunday diet of many a quite respectable family, affected him with a slightly disgusted incredulity which he found hard to conceal; fortunately, however, such things belonged mainly to a world with which Browdley had little in common.

Then, with a jerk of inward perception, he passed from bewilderment to personal misgiving. Here was a girl, a daughter of one of his own chapel officials, proposing to do something monstrously unwise (quite apart from any question of morals); and he, the Reverend Howat Freemantle, was stirred by the matter to no more profound emotion than a sort of peeved fastidiousness. It was rather as if Ringwood, meeting a man bleeding to death by the roadside, should pass by for fear of getting Ms clothes soiled. After all, what was the good of his pastorate if he couldn't make himself of use in such an emergency? He thought, with a quick return of his old self-upbraiding mood: Oh yes, you're all right for giving addresses about Mozart and drinking tea with the ladies, but when it comes to tackling the practical sort of work that justifies the rather eccentric costume you wear and the prefix to your name, then you fail utterly and hopelessly. Really, really, you aren't going to let a girl of twenty-two run off with a married man of fifty...or are you? (He answered himself: But you can't stop her; she's over age; she has the legal right to do what she wants and she knows it.) But, man, you can stop her, or you've got to try, anyhow. She's given you a loophole; she's sent you an address; there's nothing, indeed, to prevent you from actually meeting her, if she'll see you, when you go to London on Friday; then you can put your persuasive eloquence to a more vital test than the luring of threepenny bits into the collecting plate. However much you dislike the job, you've got to see that girl, you've got to talk her into her right senses, and you've got to make her return home. (But then, Garland says he won't have her back at any price.) Nonsense; he will, or, if he says he won't, then you've got another job--to persuade *him*. And in any case, whether he relents or not, your duty with the girl is plain...

Howat was thoroughly wretched by the time he returned to the Manse for tea. He had made up his mind that he would not and could not shirk his duty, but he felt no sort of enthusiasm about it, still less any confidence of being successful. It was all so extraordinary, so unpleasantly removed from his usual 'beat'. During the past dozen years there had been many occasions on which he had had to exert his personal influence in some cause or other, but they had all been interventions of a more straightforward kind--pleading with an employer not to prosecute in a case of theft, arranging terms of peace between landlord and tenant, telling youths they oughtn't to spend so much money in the public-houses, and so on. But this affair was clearly different in kind as well as in degree.

That evening there took place in the chapel the customary week-night service, and for perhaps the first time in his life Howat gave an address which he knew, while he was speaking, did not represent the best that was in him. The subject was 'prayer', and he heard, with dismay, his own voice, perfectly fluent and modulated, dispensing a representative selection of all the more obvious platitudes that had ever been coined on the topic.

He wished, while he was leading the singing of the last hymn, that he could remember more about the girl. He couldn't even picture her in his mind, but then, he had never had a good memory for faces. All he recollected (rather oddly, in the circumstances) was that she had seemed to him quite normal and pleasant.

He felt so sure that he would not easily sleep that night that after making cocoa in the kitchen he took the cup to his study, and settled himself in his favourite armchair. But in such a solitude he was more than ever at the mercy of upbraiding conscience; he knew that he must, inevitably, see the girl, and he could no longer even shirk the necessary details of fixing an appointment. In the end (about midnight) he took pen and paper and wrote the following:

"DEAR MISS GARLAND,-I received your letter, but before attempting to do what you ask, I would rather like to talk things over with you. It happens that I shall be in London on Friday of this week-- could you meet me, say, at Charing Cross post office at 5.30 p.m.? There will not be time for you to write in answer, so I will hope to see you there if you can manage it."

As he read this over he had the ignoble thought: Maybe she won't come; she'll guess I mean to argue with her and try to get her back...And that, after another troubled bout with his conscience, made him compose a much shorter note--merely:

"DEAR MISS GARLAND,-I shall be in London on Friday-- can you meet me at Charing Cross post office at 5.30 p.m.? There will not be time for you to reply to me here, but I will hope to see you if you can possibly manage it."

It was almost one o'clock when he went out to post the letter. Caution advised him not to drop it in the pillar-box at the corner of School Lane; the Browdley post office was notorious as a centre of gossip and scandal-mongering. Instead he walked to a small wall-box about a mile away in the country and in a different postal area. A tired wakefulness was on him, and his throat was giving pain again; well, never mind, in another couple of days he would know the truth about that. The walk calmed him a little; the night was cold and clear, and even the badly-proportioned façade of the chapel loomed with a certain dignity into the blue-black sky. The theme of the song he had been composing that morning recurred, but somehow failed to satisfy--poor stuff now, remembered against a background of pain and starlight that seemed to throb in rhythmic unison together.

Back at the Manse he thought of the earlier draft of his letter, thrown into the wastepaper-basket; safer, perhaps, to burn it. He did so, with difficulty in the dying embers of the fire, and afterwards, on sudden impulse, opened the drawer of his desk which contained the Raphael picture. He stared at it for a moment, almost as if he hoped it would tell him something; then, after a faint sigh, nothing was left but to put it away, turn out the light, and go to bed.

CHAPTER FOUR - THURSDAY

He had slept poorly; his throat was bad again; and the bacon and eggs, due to renewed miscalculation or negligence on the part of Ellen, were almost uneatable. He did not grumble, partly because Mary grumbled so much, but chiefly because he had no appetite. "I suppose you'll be wanting your breakfast early tomorrow, Howat?" Aunt Viney said, but he replied: "Oh no, I'll make myself a cup of tea before I go--I can get a meal on the train. There's no need for you or Ellen to get up any earlier than usual." He disliked giving trouble, not wholly from unselfish motives--he disliked the trouble that giving trouble caused.

After breakfast he had hoped for an hour or so of quietness; as it chanced, however, several callers took up his time; a woman wanted a 'character' written out for her small boy, a Sunday school pupil; and an unemployed young fellow, a complete stranger, called to know if Howat could give him some job of painting or cleaning windows in the chapel. Howat couldn't, but the man's long story of tramping the country in search of work depressed him in a way which the narrator joyfully perceived; he amplified his tale till Howat was finally reduced to a condition of nodding melancholy. In the end a ten-shilling note, which Howat could ill afford, changed hands, and the man was sent to the kitchen to see if he could be given a meal. He got one, but Aunt Viney meanwhile put him through various tests of her own devising, with the result that, so she claimed afterwards to Mrs. Freemantle, she felt sure he was a fraud--"though, of course, you can never prove these things, and Howat had given him something, I'll dare be bound, as he always does unless I catch them first before they get inside the house."

Afterwards came a professional call from Salcombe, the Wesleyan minister at the other end of the town--a large, grey-bearded man with a harsh voice and a curious trick of fidgeting with his pince-nez all the time he was speaking. He wanted to talk to Howat about the Armistice Day service; Howat, he understood, had charge of the hymns; what hymns were going to be chosen? Something well-known, of course; and if he, Salcombe, might be excused for making a few suggestions...Howat found that Salcombe had everything most accurately mapped out--he wanted this hymn and that, and this and that verse omitted--all, naturally, for reasons which he was quite prepared to explain in detail. Howat, however, saved him the trouble by a swift and comprehensive acquiescence; yes, quite; exactly; he was perfectly agreeable; oh, most certainly, just so, just so. And Salcombe went home afterwards and remarked to his wife at lunch (they took dinner in the evening): "By the way, I called on Freemantle this morning, my dear. I got my way with him about those hymns. An easy man to deal with, if only one uses a little tact."

About a quarter-past eleven Howat went out; he had several calls to make in the town. One was at the bank; he cashed a cheque on his own private account for twenty pounds (more than enough, he reckoned, for the London trip, including the cost of a new suit of clothes, if he should decide to buy one, and the highest conceivable specialist's fee.) Then visited the library, verified the times of his trains the next morning, and chose another batch of books for young Trevis. The boy read so fast it was difficult to keep up with him, but at length Howat made a selection which he hoped would please--Haldane's "Possible Worlds", and two novels, Hergesheimer's "Java Head" and one called "Brown on Resolution" by a writer named Forrester. Those ought to last Trevis over the week-end, anyway. He went round to Mansion Street with them and spent an hour or so chatting with the boy, whom he found at first in a rather depressed mood. Before leaving, he asked if there were anything Trevis would like him to bring back from London--"I shan't be there more than a few hours, but I'll have time to run round the shops, if there's anything you think you'd care about."

Trevis answered, rather sadly: "If it isn't too much trouble you could bring me a London evening paper--I haven't seen one since I left Cambridge. And it'll only cost threepence if you get them all. There's nothing else I want, thanks all the same."

"Right, then. I won't forget. And you can expect me round with them on Monday morning."

He shook hands and was just going out of the room when Trevis called back: "Oh, by the way--any more news about that girl of Garland's?"

Howat answered: "Nothing very definite, I'm afraid. Only rumours which perhaps I oughtn't to repeat."

"No need--I've probably heard them. They say the man's a dreadful creature fat little Jew with a bald head and gold teeth. So they say, mind you But I thought you might know something."

Howat shook his head. "I wish I did. Who gave you that description of the man?"

"Our maid had it from one of the neighbours, and heaven knows where she got it."

"It's extraordinary--if it's true."

"Yes, isn't it? But then, Elizabeth was always an extraordinary girl." There was a pause, after which Howat continued, with growing intensity: "It's not only extraordinary, it's--it's monstrous. A young girl barely out of her teens and a man--like that--married--twice her age--"

"But I suppose it all counts for nothing when two people reckon themselves to be in love."

"*Love?*"

Howat uttered the word incredulously, as if it were the last that would ever have occurred to him in such a connection. Even its very sound, though he enunciated it often enough in his public prayers and sermons, had a way of seeming different when uttered in a small room and in the course of casual conversation. *Love*, indeed? Love to him was the feeling he had for his wife, and which he presumed other men had for their wives; he understood it as such; it was a straightforward, simple feeling, perfectly reasonable and devoid of complication. Whereas this feeling of Elizabeth Garland for her paramour (the quaintly old-fashioned term was the only one he could bring to mind) must be something altogether different, something totally and mercifully outside his own and most other people's personal experience.

He said, abruptly: "Good-bye, Trevis, must get away--so many odd things to do before tomorrow. I won't forget those papers for you...And as for that other matter--the one we've just been discussing I'm afraid it's useless to theorise. Perhaps things may not turn out as badly as we fear. Good-bye, now, until Monday." Then he went home to dinner at the Manse.

He was busy all afternoon; it was amazing how even a projected absence of two days entailed all sorts of arrangings and postponements, letters to this person and that, instructions, suggestions, and excuses. He was by nature a hard and enthusiastic worker, and Browdley had well learnt that if there were a charity concert to be organised, a subscription to be raised, a movement to be launched, a defunct society to be resuscitated, or any particularly tiresome or exasperating piece of work to be done, the Reverend Howat Freemantle could usually be relied upon for the job. It was not that he enjoyed the fuss and bother of such things (quite the contrary, indeed), but it was always easy to persuade him that they were duties that someone ought to do, and that if he didn't tackle them, probably nobody would. It was known, too, that once he had set his hand to a task, he never flagged, never complained, and never shirked responsibility.

64

So, during a dozen years, his life had gradually become more fretfully busy, nor had he developed to any degree the art of delegating authority and leaving odd jobs to subordinates. He was old-fashioned, too, in his methods; a telephone would have been a help to him, but he believed he could not afford it, and he still wrote out all his letters by hand. He would sometimes have welcomed assistance from his daughter, but he felt that she had her own work to do, and he did not care to ask her. Often, when a succession of exacting trivialities tired him out completely, he would feel that he really must cut down some of his societies; but when he began to think out which ones to cut, he always found the problem far too hard. Enthusiasm, indeed, was ever ready in him to rise up at the mere thought of neglecting or abandoning anything.

This afternoon, this Thursday afternoon, he found the hundred and one urgencies of the moment producing in him that familiar mood of tired resentment. One of his activities was the treasurership of a Savings Certificate Club; children at day and Sunday school brought their pennies to him or to Mary, and the accumulation was invested at the local post office. All this required careful booking, and now, he discovered, as he went through the records, Mary had let things get in a muddle. After over an hour of exceedingly tiresome reckoning he succeeded in restoring the club to solvency by means of a grant from his own pocket of three and ten-pence. It was annoying, and he was, so far as he could ever be, annoyed. If Mary had been there in the house he might even have addressed her strongly; but she was out, and he could only feel vaguely out of humour with himself and things in general. Really, he reflected, surveying the litter on his desk that represented work both finished and unfinished, he would have to prune away a lot of his routine work; he felt like a pioneer in a tropical jungle, growing weaker every moment while the enveloping foliage became denser and harder to penetrate. There was the Antiquarian Society, which always for some reason sent him the most troublesome Latin documents to translate he knew Latin, it was true, but he was no particular scholar--why couldn't the Grammar School masters try their hands at that sort of thing? And the Tennis Club (he wasn't interested in tennis and couldn't imagine why they had asked him to be secretary), and the local League of Nations Society (he was interested in the League of Nations, but there were other people who ought to be able to do the job of President quite as adequately), and the Hospital Sunday Fund (a splendid thing, doubtless, but why didn't some of his professional colleagues take their turn with it?)--he reviewed them all in his mind, one after the other, and wondered which obligation he could get rid of with least commotion.

And then, on top of it all, and in addition to that annoying three and ten-pence, came the thought of the morrow--the early rise, the walk through the dark streets to the station, bag in hand, the crawling local train, the ride across Manchester in a tram, the express to London, booking a room at a hotel, visiting the heating-apparatus people in the afternoon, then the appointment with the specialist, and after that, if she turned up, his meeting with that girl at Charing Cross. What a day! It was the last two items that seemed most to be feared, and perhaps even of the last two, the vision of the Wimpole Street consulting-room did not trouble him quite so much as the thought of what he would have to say to the girl. Yet he felt, with slow rage inside him: This is my real work, this job of saving souls--this one job which I shirk is the real thing I'm here for. All this other stuff, this parade of being busy that makes many a parson think he's a success when he's really only doing a clerk's job--all this merely disguises the real issue-- the fact that if I fail in this Garland affair, I fail utterly. These societies and clubs and meetings and such-like have been a veil hiding life from me and me from life; after all my years of ministerial work, I don't know where I am when I'm faced with something out of the ordinary; I don't understand the mainsprings of human conduct, probably not as well as young Trevis, certainly not as well as Ringwood or the Catholic priest...

Towards twilight he took his letters to the pillar-box, and after posting them walked along School Lane as far as the edge of the town, despite a light rain that was falling. The problem of what he should say to Elizabeth Garland and how he should persuade her to return to Browdley, was more than perplexing; it was beginning to be an obsession. All the so far known and meagrely reported ingredients of the affair danced before his mind like animated fragments of a jig-saw puzzle--the Raphael picture she had sent him, the fuss with Garland, her letter from London, and Trevis's description of the fat little Jew fiddler with the bald head and the gold teeth. What was it that she or any girl could feel for such a man? Some kind of physical infatuation? But there once more he was in uncharted seas, wondering at the sort of desire that could so outweigh considerations of home, family, position, and morals.

He tried even to recollect his own desires, so far as he had ever been conscious of them; and, though he felt it almost sacrilegious to do so, he cast back in memory to his early days of courtship and marriage. Of course he had always loved his wife, and he was still, he would have said, 'in love' with her; but he recognised, nevertheless, that there was a fiercer passion that belonged peculiarly to youth. In his own life it had coincided with his 'conversion', and when he tried to think of those early days he had a vision of peaceful evening walks across fields to chapel, with Mary by his side; he could not, at such a distance in time, recollect exactly what had been his feelings during those walks, but he was quite certain that the course of true love, in his case, had been exceptionally smooth.

As for temptation of any kind since marriage, he could honestly and with confidence assert that he had never even known what it was; indeed, the mere contemplation of it was distasteful. Yet there was a world, he knew, in which unpleasant things of that sort did abound--a strange world in which Elizabeth Garland, for one, was dangerously adrift, and which lay pitilessly beyond the scope of all the societies of which he was president and secretary. He dared not, merely to preserve his own comfort, shirk total knowledge of that world; on the contrary, it might sometimes be his unpleasant duty to explore.

He went home for tea, and in the evening there was the weekly Brotherhood Meeting. His throat, which was definitely worse, gave him a good excuse for not attending, but he would not take it; he went, sang, spoke, and made his throat so painful that it kept him awake for half the night. In the early morning darkness of his bedroom he felt desperately afraid of all that the coming day might bring, and when at last he fell asleep and dreamed, his dreams were of restless, inexplicable things.

CHAPTER FIVE - FRIDAY MORNING AND AFTERNOON

Unless on some definitely professional errand Howat always travelled in mufti. He did so quite openly, even sometimes when he went no further than Manchester, and though many of his colleagues in the town did not approve, the lay population were quite accustomed to seeing him dressed as one of themselves. "There's something about a parson's collar that puts people off," Howat had once said to Doxley, of the Congregational Church, "especially in such a confined space as a railway compartment, where they have nothing to do but stare. It makes them uncomfortable among themselves, they feel under constraint with one another--they either talk at' you, or else relapse into a brooding silence which you can feel to be anti-clerical. When I was a young fellow, just beginning, I used to wear the whitest and highest of clerical collars because I was so proud of my profession, but now I think I'm less proud of that than I am of my common humanity. I feel that if I've got to wear something that marks me out as different or superior to others, then in fairness to them I ought to travel first-class--like officers in the army."

"But surely," Doxley had said, "that argument would apply just as much against wearing the clerical habit at all, even in Browdley?"

"Not quite. In Browdley, I'm on business, as it were--my professional badge is as appropriate as a doctor's black bag or a collier's black face. But when I'm shopping, say, in Manchester, or on holiday at the seaside, then I'd feel as unseemly in my parson's rig-out as a judge if he had to play golf in his wig and gown."

"You mean that when you're out of Browdley, you don't want people to know what you are?"

"Well, I don't see why I should fling my profession in their faces, anyhow." Doxley always put Howat in the impish mood of the small boy who knocks at doors and then runs away; he had added, then, with a touch of that impishness: "I consider it an impertinence to approach strangers with a sort of label tied on to you saying--' Beware! I'm not an ordinary person like you'."

And as the Reverend Jefferson Doxley had never for a moment believed himself to be an ordinary person like anyone else, the argument had here tapered away into an infinite shaft of disagreement. Doxley had, however, said one thing that Howat afterwards remembered. "Well, Freemantle, whatever you say, you can't deny that a parson's collar does mean something to people; they look on it as a guarantee of character, even if they pretend to scoff at it. Take, for instance, the case of some timid, nervous girl walking alone along a country lane late at night. She sees a man approaching her in the distance, wonders who and what he is, begins to feel rather terrified, and then--suddenly--sees that collar. Don't you think it's a relief? She may be agnostic or an atheist or anything you like, but she knows she needn't be afraid of meeting a parson in the dark."

"It seems a rather negative tribute to parsons in general," Howat had answered, still impishly. That conversation had taken place some half-dozen years before, since when Doxley had never wholly 'approved of' his brother minister; he suspected him, indeed, of being dangerously imbued with eccentric, undignified, and even socialistic ideas.

But now, on this Friday morning in November as the Manchester-London express raced over the plains of Northamptonshire, there could have seemed little eccentric, much less dangerous, in the quiet, tired-looking man who took lunch by himself at the far end of the dining-car. He had been sleeping for part of the journey, and there were lines beneath his eyes that made many a traveller, especially women, give him a fleetingly compassionate glance as they hurried along the centre aisle. There was something in his face that curiously attracted most people--a sort of rather sad winsomeness that made them feel they could rely on him for infinite depths of sympathy and understanding. Though, as a matter of fact, he did not always understand as well as they imagined; people often poured out intimate personal confessions to which his carefully kind attention was only a mask to cover up extreme uncomfortableness and a bewildered lack of comprehension.

He took coffee and a cigarette after lunch (he only very rarely smoked, and never knew quite whether it gave him any pleasure or not); then he looked through the *Manchester Guardian*, and tried to interest himself in the passing scenes of the countryside; but soon his head was slipping forward again and he dozed fitfully till the train slowed down for the terminus.

After leaving the train he walked to an hotel in Southampton Row, at which he had stayed on the occasion of his first overnight visit to London as a youth. It consisted of three adjacent Georgian houses, a good deal spoiled in the process of conversion into one establishment, and always smelling (more or less, according to the time of day) of cabbage and floor-polish. Its principal and perhaps only merits were that it was cheap (seven-and-six for bed-and-breakfast), respectable, and near the big northern railway stations.

This last was an important consideration for Howat, who reckoned himself unable to afford cabs (he knew little about the prices of things and had never bothered to discover that London taxis were only half as expensive as those in Manchester and about a quarter the cost of hiring any sort of car in Browdley).

Having lunched on the train, he had nothing to do at the hotel except book a room. They gave him a small low-ceilinged, top-floor apartment, overlooking the roof of a garage, sparingly but perhaps just adequately furnished for its purpose, with a shilling-in-the-slot gas-fire, and an electric light in the most difficult of all positions for either tying a tie or reading in bed. Howat hurriedly dumped down his bag; it was already two o'clock (the train had been rather late); he must get along to those engineering people. In the hotel lobby as he descended, the proprietress called to him to sign the register; he did so, writing 'Howat Freemantle, Browdley, British' in his usual clear script. He disliked the title 'Reverend' and never used it of himself, though he could not prevent others doing so. He disliked it for a certain pretentiousness it seemed to have, just as he never much cared for the word 'study' as applied to the room at home in which he worked.

It was a fine day, fortunately, for it had been intermittently on his mind throughout the journey that he had forgotten to bring an umbrella. He boarded a bus outside the hotel and rode to Aldwych; then he changed to another bus and got down at Mansion House station. It was a quarter to three when he arrived at the showrooms and city headquarters of Neal & Sons, Sanitary, Hydraulic, and Central Heating Engineers. In another hour and a quarter, he reflected, he would be arriving at Wimpole Street. Another hour and a quarter of uncertainty, followed, perhaps, by a certainty that would be even more dreadful. He felt his throat like something burning and malevolent that did not belong to him; he was sure now, with a sudden inward lurch of panic, that the verdict would be all that he had feared.. As he gave his name to the clerk in the outside office he heard his own voice as that of another man speaking; he wondered if he would be able to mobilise his wits for this earlier interview. The clerk ushered him through an inner office into the presence of a smartly dressed and very shining, voluble person who shook him eagerly by the hand, offered him an arm-chair, and proceeded to talk in a hearty way about the weather. "And was it raining in Manchester when you came through this morning, Mr. Freemantle? Ha, Ha!" The weather, politics, bad trade, and finally, as if with apologies that such an irrelevant thing should after all be mentioned, this question of a new heating apparatus.

Howat sat back and wished that the chair were not such an easy chair; he was in grave danger of falling into a sleep, or at any rate, into a dream; he kept hearing the other man's voice and had to wonder whether he were still just talking or had begun to ask questions that demanded answers. "Well, Mr. Freemantle, we could probably do you quite a satisfactory system for a hundred pounds or so--of course I couldn't give an exact quotation till our man has been up to see the place. I can assure you we're used to the job just take a look at this catalogue--it contains merely a few examples of churches and chapels throughout the country that have given us their heating contract..." Howat fingered the smooth, glossy pages and had a misty vision of one church after another--plain-looking churches with oblong windows, elaborate-looking churches with stone facings and Gothic stained-glass, churches with stone crosses, churches without stone crosses, churches surrounded by a litter of schoolrooms and vestries, churches with turrets, cupolas, even (so it appeared) minarets, churches with machicolated towers, crocheted spires, and Ionic porticoes, churches enveloped by apparently tropical verdure, churches with the minister standing on the front step, churches of all sizes, denominations, architectures, and degrees of prosperity. It had hardly seemed possible that there could be so many churches in the world, and all, it appeared, were warmed by radiators supplied by Neal and Sons.

Howat said at length: "Well, yes, I think it will be all right. We shall be very glad to have your system."

"I can promise you, sir, that both you and your congregation will be well pleased with it."

"Oh, I'm sure, I'm sure."

"A good heating apparatus, sir, is half the battle, I always think. Warm your church well and people will flock into it. How can people worship when their feet are cold?"

"Quite--oh, quite." At any other time Howat might have found it refreshing to talk to this enthusiastic young fellow, and even to discuss with him such vital matters as he had just touched upon; but as it was, he felt anxious at all costs to end the interview. He said: "Perhaps, then, you'll get on with the job as soon as you can, eh?"

The other seemed genuinely grieved by this display of haste. "Would you care to step down into the basement, sir, and see the kind of installations we put in? We have a few models on view and we can also show you the apparatus that actually heats this office, and is heating it at the present moment--identical, of course, with the type we shall he supplying to you. I think you'll admit, sir, that the temperature of this room is just about what one would wish for."

Too hot, Howat thought sleepily--far too hot; but he said: "Oh yes, just about right."

"We can regulate it, of course. A single turn of the knob--like this--"

Howat watched him rather sadly. Was it merely professional, such enthusiasm? Did the youth go home and dream about heating-apparatus? Did heating-apparatus fill a 'niche in his soul? Howat felt: I wish at this present moment I could believe in anything as fervently as this fellow seems to believe in these pipes and radiators...

"Perhaps, sir, you would care to come down and inspect--"

Howat rose and shook his head sombrely. "Well, no, I don't think I'll bother, if you don't mind. I--I have several other appointments this afternoon, and not much time left for them. Your apparatus, I have no doubt, will suit us admirably. I'd better be getting along now."

"Very good, sir. And when would it be convenient for us to send our man up to Browdley?"

"Your man? Oh yes, about the pipes and things--yes--oh, any time next week would do."

"Very good, Mr. Freemantle. We will advise you definitely by postcard. Good-bye, sir--very pleased indeed to have met you."

And in another moment Howat was outside in the street again. It was nearly half-past three.

He boarded a bus at the corner and rode past the Temple and Charing Cross and up Regent Street. By that time it was ten minutes to four, and at Oxford Circus he took to the pavements and began to thread his way diagonally into that stately district almost equally consecrated to music and medicine. He tried to think of the concert he might attend that evening, and of his more immediate rendezvous at Charing Cross at half-past five; but he hardly succeeded in either effort; a greater imminence was on him, a vertical barrier of time beyond which even futurity seemed scarcely to exist. He knew now that this interview with the specialist had been an unrealised background of all his thoughts and emotions for weeks. He felt beyond panic just numb with a secret, paralysing excitement of mind.

It was a few minutes past the hour when he rang the bell beside the massive blue-enamelled door. He recalled the last time he had been there, ten years before, when his youngest boy had been discovered tubercular; it had been Blenkiron's partner then whom he had seen, and he had still a memory of the old man, and of his calm and somehow almost reassuring way of telling a father that his boy was seriously affected. He remembered coming out of the house with the boy's hand in his; they had walked aimlessly round a few corners, and had then had muffins for tea in a small café, which he was sure he would never be able to find again, even if it still existed. Eighteen months after that, the boy had died.

Now, he thought, waiting for the door to open, it was *his* turn. The door swung back; he gave his name to the maid; he was shown into the same room, with the same furnishings--exactly the same, they looked, despite the fact that the old man had died in the interval and his assistant-partner had succeeded to the practice. There was certainly the same ormolu clock on the mantelpiece and the same locked bookcase full of richly bound copies of Dickens, Thackeray, and Lord Lytton. Howat put his hat and gloves on the table with a gesture almost of familiarity, and the maid, as she left him, switched on a cluster of lights that hardly illumined the room so much as extinguished the fading daylight outside.

The clock ticked on; and he knew, as he listened to it, that he was no longer nervous at all, but just calm, frozenly calm, and ready for whatever fate might send. Even the pain in his throat had merged into that all-enveloping numbness of sensation.

The door opened, and there half-entered a man of rather more than middle-age, keen-faced and handsome in conventional morning-dress. He shook hands with Howat, and guided him into an inner room.

Half an hour later the examination, which had been very thorough, was finished. Blenkiron sat in his swivel desk-chair, with his long fingers splayed out on the shining mahogany. He looked as if he could not quite decide how to begin. So far he had hardly spoken at all, except to ask questions. Howat faced him steadfastly from an armchair opposite; he was pale, excited, and twitching about the mouth as he sometimes did when he began sermons.

"I understand, Mr. Freemantle," mused Blenkiron at length, "that you decided to consult me because my late partner, Doctor Newsome, once examined your son?"

"Yes. It was the only medical address in London I knew."

"Quite." A faint superciliousness edged round the doctor's clear--cut lips. "And you have a great deal of faith, I suppose, in a London medical address?"

"Perhaps one has, rather naturally."

Blenkiron smiled and began to fidget with a brass paper-weight. "Well, well, I wonder whether one ought to say so--but it's a fact, you know, that there are some exceedingly clever doctors and surgeons in the provinces. Liverpool, Birmingham, Manchester--really, I could give you names in those cities, but of course I won't--dear me, no. It is a most gratifying and profitable superstition that the best medical brains in this country are all congregated in the region bounded by Oxford Street and the Marylebone Road. Only a superstition, of course, but I don't know what we doctors would do without it. I suppose you think that every brass plate in Wimpole Street and Harley Street means a fabulous income? Not at all--the superstition has shown signs of waning in recent years. Believe me, there are men in this road who can hardly find the cash for their quarterly telephone bills."

Howat nodded and wished he would get to the point. Doctors seemed to enjoy keeping their patients in suspense as long as possible--as a nerve test, perhaps? Blenkiron caught the impatient glance and went on: "But these are digressions, are they not? By the way, Mr. Freemantle, how is your boy now? It was--let me see--what was the trouble exactly?"

"He died. It was consumption."

"Oh, that's bad, very bad. I didn't realise." He paused, apparently for deep thought, and then added: "And I understand that you yourself are a clergyman in Browdley?"

"A minister--a Nonconformist minister."

"I don't know the town, but I gather from the papers that trade has been very bad lately in that part of the country. I suppose cotton is the black spot."

"Yes."

"And coal? Have you any coal mines?"

"Several in the district."

"And I don't suppose you've ever been down one, eh? You're just as bad as some of us Londoners. I had a titled person consulting me yesterday--I won't tell you his name, but he's very well known in politics--he confessed to me that he had never yet been inside the Tower of London. As I never had either, we were able to share the deep disgrace...However, that is rather by the by...Are you happy in your work in Browdley? Have you any particular worries--professional worries, I mean?"

"No more than most parsons, I should think."

"You work hard, no doubt?"

"I try to."

"Yes, of course. And you have to talk a good deal in public, that's rather inevitable, isn't it?"

"It is, I'm afraid, yes."

"Well, you'll have to drop doing so much of it for a time. I don't suppose you're surprised to hear me tell you that, eh?...Is your wife living?"

"Yes."

"And in good health?"

"Fairly good. She's not strong, I'm sorry to say.

"And your children--have you any other children?"

"I have a boy--in Canada--and a girl, who lives at home."

"They are both well?"

"The girl is. The boy--well, we haven't heard from him for several years."

"Really? Perhaps he'll come romping home someday with his pockets bulging with banknotes. They do sometimes, you know."

"I should be glad to see him whether his pockets were bulging or not."

"Ah, yes, of course...What would you do, though, if he did strike lucky and make you a present of a few thousand pounds? I suppose you'd rebuild your church or something of the sort."

"I don't know. I've never considered it."

"I thought you clergymen always knew what to do with money?...But tell me now, coming back to the point, do you often have headaches?"

"Fairly often."

"And your eyes--have they been tested lately?"

"About a year or so ago."

"Do you enjoy your food?"

"Moderately."

Only moderately?"

"I don't think I ever was very keen on eating and drinking."

"Are you an abstainer?"

"Yes."

"Perhaps that accounts for your not being keen on drinking, eh? Seriously, though, it's a pity you don't enjoy good food. Do you like corn on the cob?"

75

"I don't think I know what it is."

"It's an American dish--they do it very well at Fouchard's, in Greek Street. It's something you oughtn't to miss during your visit to London. You eat it, you know, with your fingers--rather like playing a mouth organ. Very messy, but extremely palatable. I have a doctor friend who says that a great part of its value lies in the mode of eating--it satisfies the atavistic desire we all have, consciously or unconsciously, to take our food in our hands and tear it to pieces with our teeth. I wonder if that is really so."

"I wonder," said Howat, without wondering at all.

Blenkiron gave the brass paperweight a little push to one side of the desk. "Well, I expect you're waiting for me to tell you something about yourself. Of course the really hard problem in such a case as yours is not 'what' but 'why'. I must confess that for the last ten minutes I've been puzzling myself over that...and I'm not much nearer an answer. You'll have to knock off most things for a time, that's clear. I daresay you know that your nervous system isn't exactly a strong spot. But what prevented you from letting your own local doctor tell you so? As for your throat, I gather it's been causing you a fair amount of worry, lately?"

"It has, yes."

"Which means, I suppose, that you've been having the same worry that ninety-nine people out of every hundred have nowadays when they feel a pain. Oh, you needn't bother to confide in me--I know all about it. Even doctors aren't immune. I made a report on one the other day--a woman doctor--she suspected she had an internal carcinoma, but it turned out she was only going to have a baby. So you see--"

"You mean, then, that there's *nothing wrong with me*?"

"My dear sir, there's a very great deal wrong with you. You are, I should say, within a very short distance of a serious nervous breakdown. But apart from that, which is quite bad enough, surely, I don't find anything much amiss--your heart and lungs are sound, you have a reasonable blood pressure, and as for the larynx--well, clergyman's sore throat is rather a vocational disease, isn't it?"

He went on to say a great deal more, but Howat did not hear him, and was hardly aware of the three pound notes that somehow escaped from his wallet and into the doctor's. The fee, in fact, was three guineas, but Howat forgot the odd shillings and Blenkiron did not remind him. Of that final handshake and the maid's guidance through the hall to the street-door Howat was almost totally unconscious; but the cold air awakened him when he found himself standing on the pavement outside the house, with his hat and gloves still in his hand and the street-lamps glittering like chains of gems in either direction. Beyond them, into the star-speckled sky loomed the tall grey houses, and a taxi came cruising slowly down that enchanted canyon. Howat raised his hand; the driver pulled up at the kerb; Howat sprang inside, without a word till the driver asked where he was to drive to; then Howat stammered--"Oh, yes, of course--the main street, where the shops are--Oxford Street, yes--oh, anywhere..."

He sat well forward on the seat and stared hard out of the window, as one who had somehow never used his eyes before. It did not even occur to him that he had never been in a London taxi before, so completely was that trivial novelty submerged in the vaster novelty of life itself. All the doubts and miseries of the last few months were lifted; the barrier was down, and life stretched ahead of him like a new dream, buoyant and zestful and rich in promise. He opened the window, despite the cold, and took in deep draughts of air that seemed to him purer than any he had ever breathed before; he could see a woman crossing the road with a pram and smiling at the baby inside it; there, over there, two men were standing at a corner reading the same newspaper and laughing; in the middle of the road a night-watchman slowly filled his pipe as he settled himself beside a brazier-fire. And suddenly, with a little swirl, the taxi turned out of that lovely tributary into the full tide of the river itself, that blazing river of shops and omnibuses and skysigns--Oxford Street. "Go on!" he shouted through the window on the driver's side, and then sank back amidst the cushions with glorious exhaustion.

The cab soon became embedded in a long line of slow-moving traffic, and he thought, during those moments, that he had never seen anything in the world so truly lovely as that pageant of shop-windows and eager happy faces. There was one window full of gorgeously tinted silks, slung rainbow-like from corner to corner, and there was a shop that had a machine in the window that twisted skeins of toffee together, and a sky-sign, high up above, that gave the weather forecast in scampering electric letters, and a huge shop-building with a frontage of Ionic columns silver-white in the upward glow of arc-lamps, and people, people--hundreds and thousands of them in one long, throbbing, colourful fresco of life itself.

And the loveliness was in his ears as well--he heard the clamour of motor-horns and the shouting of newsboys and all the mingled noises of streets and houses like some triumphant symphony on a new theme; he wanted to join in it, to lean his head out of the window and shout to someone in sheer exultation; and then he thought: Steady,

77

Steady--keep calmer--you've got a happy evening before you--there's that concert--have you forgotten it? They're playing Brahms...and all at once, with that little twist of recollection, his mind was flooded with imagined melody, and he saw himself, as in those ridiculous boyhood dreams, standing on a conductor's rostrum, baton in hand, controlling a world of his own creation.

There were trees now, iron railings, vistas of glittering head-lights, and a faint smell of wood-smoke on the air; then he caught sight of a clock--twenty-five past five--and suddenly remembered that business at Charing Cross. His spirits fell momentarily at the thought, but rose again almost instantly and with new intensity, for his imagination transformed him magically from the conductor of an orchestra into an orator of burning zeal, a Peter the Hermit and Savonarola combined, whose impassioned pleadings no sinner could hope to resist. He was certain now that he would meet that girl, talk to her, convince her, and have her returning to Browdley that very night; there was no longer any doubt about it; he could not fail with this new and god-like strength that was in him. He put his head out of the window and called to the driver--" Charing Cross--the post office--as quick as you can!"

It was beginning to be the evening 'rush' period, and the taxi was held up many times, at the Marble. Arch, at Berkeley Street, and for several minutes at Piccadilly Circus. It was nearly a quarter to six when Howat stepped to the pavement at the corner of Trafalgar Square; he was rather excited by that time; perhaps she hadn't come, or had got tired of waiting; he paid the driver, adding a far too lavish tip, and found him-self staring vacantly at buses and sky-signs and a pavement artist's drawings of Ramsay MacDonald and Lloyd George; it was an absurd place, he reflected, as he became conscious of the crowds all about him, to have fixed for meeting anyone, especially someone he didn't know very well.

He had been staring about for several minutes when he felt a hand touching his arm. He looked round and saw a girl, and though he knew immediately that it was Elizabeth Garland, he was certain he would never have recognised her of his own accord. Really, it was as if he had never seen her before.

CHAPTER SIX - FRIDAY TEA

"Good evening, Mr. Freemantle," she said, in a slow soft-toned voice (it was as if, too, he had never heard it before), and he said "Good evening" and observed her rather incredulously. A certain sense of the extraordinariness of the situation came over him, and with a little effort he made himself recollect how matters stood--he a Browdley parson meeting a young girl at Charing Cross to persuade her not to run away to Paris with an elderly Jew with a bald head and gold teeth (he could not unfix that graphic picture from his mind). But the picture gave him renewed and indignant confidence; by God, he thought, glancing at her again, she mustn't do a thing like that; it would be worse than an offence against morals, it would be--and then he checked himself and wondered what *could* be worse than an offence against morals? Dimly he felt that something could be, and the feeling, obscure and transient, linked itself with all the new and astonishing perceptions that were invading him from all directions. By God, no, she mustn't; he must prevent her, at all costs. And, as earnestly as he had ever prayed for anything, he prayed, wordlessly, for strength to achieve that end.

"I got your letter," she was saying, returning his glance with one just as curious. "It was nice of you to think of meeting me. Are you in London for long?"

"I go back to-morrow. Just a business visit. I'm afraid I must have kept you waiting a long time--the traffic delayed me. What a crowd there is here!"

"Yes," she agreed. They were still standing exactly where they had met, on the edge of the pavement, surrounded by eddies of omni-buses, cabs, and pedestrians. "Have you had tea?" she continued. "Because if not we might find it quieter inside a café."

"Ah, a good idea." He had forgotten all about tea himself and was relieved by the suggestion. It would be easier, no doubt, than talking in the streets. There was a Lyons tea-shop within a few yards of them, and they made their way to it, finding a couple of scats at a small table in a corner of a first-floor room. In the sudden brilliance of electric lights his eyes were dazzled at first, but as soon as he could see her clearly again he felt indignation and determination rising in him to fever-point--she must not, must not, do a thing like that--it was monstrous, a sin more certainly a sin than anything he could ever have imagined. He wondered how he should broach the matter, whether directly or by oblique remarks; or whether, during tea, he had better let the talk remain just casual. But it was she who left him no choice, for she said, almost straightway: "Did you give my message at home, Mr. Freemantle?"

He shook his head. "I'm afraid I didn't." Then he went on, slowly and with not half the fluency he had hoped for: "The fact is, you don't seem to realise what--what a commotion you have caused by--by leaving home like this."

"Has there been such a terrible fuss?"

"Well, naturally. What else could you have expected? Your parents are both extremely upset, and I would gladly have conveyed your message if I had thought it would relieve their minds at all. Unfortunately it seemed to me quite likely to make matters worse, which was why--or one of the reasons why, at any rate--I didn't do as you suggested."

"You mean that they wouldn't have been relieved to learn that I'm all right and quite happy?"

"Well, that's not quite the way to put it. You must remember how deeply you have hurt their pride as well as their affections. I saw your father the other day, and I found him in a very angry mood about you. After all, you can understand that, I'm sure. He feels you have disgraced him. But I still think it possible--even probable--that if you were to go back now, immediately, giving up all--all that you have in mind--they would be reasonable with you. At least I can promise that I would do my best to smooth matters over."

"That's very kind indeed of you, Mr. Freemantle, but really, you know, I haven't the slightest intention of going back. You mustn't think I'm repentant or anything like that. I'd like to be on good terms with them if it's possible--that's why I wrote to you--but I can't alter my plans."

He faced her solemnly for a long moment and then said: "I hope you realise that unless you do go back, your parents arc quite determined to have nothing more to do with you--ever."

"Well, I suppose if they take up that rather silly attitude, I'll have to make the best of it, that's all."

"Make the best of it and go back?"

"No. Make the best of it and stay away."

She spoke so calmly that he just stared at her in amazement and then replied: "You really mean that--quite finally?"

"Why, of course. I do Hope you haven't made a special journey here just to try to argue me round."

"Oh, no, no--not at all." He seemed tremendously eager to convince her of that. "Oh no, you see, I had to come to London to make arrangements for a new heating apparatus we are having .installed in the chapel--it was just an idea of mine that, since you were in London also, we might meet and talk things over. I'm sorry you're so determined--I had hoped, you see--" And all the time he was stammering these and similar things, he felt: You've failed, You've bungled it all, You can do nothing with her! Where's that marvellous eloquence you were going to employ? You're no use, and why, in Heaven's name, should you ever have imagined you could be? Does anybody decide on a course of action as important as hers is and then give it up because a parson comes along with a few tea-table platitudes? And suddenly, with a new note in his voice, he leaned towards her across the table and began to speak, not with his usual easy flow of words, but in sharp, broken sentences and in a voice husky with disappointment: "My dear girl, I'm not preaching at you--don't think that--I don't want you to think I'm talking to you as a parson just, shall we say, as a friend--a friend rather older than you--though even that I won't plead too strongly, because in some ways I'm nearly as much a stranger to life as you are. Perhaps you don't know what I mean by that--well, never mind, it doesn't matter--it's a side issue. What I feel is that I want to talk to you--perhaps impertinently, in a way--I want to tell you how this course that you're taking strikes me, as a complete outsider. It's difficult, really, for me to express what I mean; I don't want to bring in the question of morals; I'd rather put it to you as a matter of wisdom-- after all, you probably believe in wisdom--you don't look at all the sort of person to act recklessly, without thinking things out beforehand--"

"I've thought out everything beforehand, I assure you."

"I know, I expected you to say that. All the same, there are times when one's thoughts aren't very reliable, when imagination loses its proper perspective, runs riot, as it were--do you know what I mean? It's like all this new mathematics--I've been reading a book about it lately. Normally we live in a Euclidian sort of world--straight lines, everything very logical, just the ordinary life that we all grow accustomed to--then, suddenly, without any warning, something gets hold of us and we go switching over into an Einstein world full of curved space and parallel lines that do meet in the end--all very marvellous and perhaps truer, in a way, than the other sort of world, but we can't afford to think so, because it wouldn't work. All I want is for you to ask yourself whether what you are going to do will work--will it be a practical success--will it--will it--do you--are you going to--" He stopped abruptly and continued, after a pause and with a slight smile: "I wonder if you really understand what I'm talking about?"

"I think I probably do," she answered cautiously, "though I'm puzzled to know why you're talking about it."

"Because I *must*, whether I offend you or not. To be quite frank, this man whom you know, whom you're proposing to go to Paris with--is he--"

Her eyes widened incredulously. "A *man*?" she interrupted. "What man? And you say I'm going to Paris with him? Really--"

"Please don't be offended. As I told you at the beginning, I don't intend to preach--"

She suddenly laughed. "But, Mr. Freemantle, it's all so utterly ridiculous! Oh, how absurd it is!" She laughed again, a little help-lessly. "I can't imagine how you got hold of such an idea. There's no man at all. I'm not going with anybody."

"You mean to say it's all untrue? You're not going to Paris with--with that man--"

"I am going abroad, certainly, but not with that man, or any man. And not, incidentally, to Paris, either. But I wish you'd tell me who that man is. I'm quite curious about him."

His eyes, watching her and her amusement, half-filled with tears, he did not know why, and all the world around him seemed drowned in the most shattering and unspeakable loveliness. "I--I don't know what to say," he stammered. "Of course I'm only going by all the talk in Browdley; how people find everything out I can't think. Some-one, I believe, saw you getting into the train at Manchester with this man--a musician, I understood--"

Her laughing was almost hysterical now. "Oh, poor Isaac--how funny he'd think it all if he knew! He plays the fiddle at a cinema in Manchester; he's married and has three children, I think--or perhaps four. He's a dear old man, and a very great friend of mine. He saw me off at the station because I had a lot of luggage to handle, and before the train started we sat in the compartment together and talked. I sup-pose that must have been when people saw us."

Howat could only stammer: "You must forgive me, forgive me."

"Why, of course, if there were anything to forgive. It's Browd-ley that's to blame, not you. Anyhow, it doesn't matter. It all makes me rather more determined that ever not to go back."

"You're not going back? You still say that?"

"Still? Why do you think I ought to change my mind?"

"I--I don't know--except that I'm sure that your parents, now that this horrible story turns out to be untrue--would be very glad--very glad indeed--to have you back."

"I'm not sure that they would, and in any case, I wouldn't be glad at all. You don't seem to realise that I don't want to go back. I've got all sorts of other plans. I'm going to Vienna to study music. Didn't you hear that? Weren't there any true rumours flying about?"

"*Music?*"

"Yes."

They stared at each other across the table amidst a curiously fateful silence. She continued, with sudden eagerness: "Oh, I'm so pleased we've cleared up all that stupid misunderstanding--we can talk to each other now just as I've wanted to for a long time. I was often on the point of telling you during those German lessons, but you never gave me the least encouragement--I had an impression you weren't interested in me and my affairs. But you're different now--I can see that--I suppose it's because you're out of Browdley. Anyhow, I must tell you all about it now that we're here together. Do you mind?"

At first she had been aloof, baffling, cordial but on the defensive; now, however, the armour dropped and a warm friendliness took its place and made him exclaim: "Mind? Good heavens, no! I want to be told the whole story--especially about the music. I'm rather interested in music myself, but I'd no idea you were. What is it, the piano?"

"No, the fiddle. I've always been keen, ever since I was a child. There was a fiddle at our house that used to belong to an uncle of mine who died, and I taught myself to play on that. I never had any lessons at first; my father didn't believe in that sort of thing. As a matter of fact, though perhaps you'll smile and won't believe it, I have an idea he thought all music, except hymn tunes and funeral marches, rather irreligious." Howat certainly did smile, and she went on, as though encouraged: "When I was fifteen I wanted to earn a living somehow or other, so I got a job in the town library--the usual graft, you know, father being a Councillor. It wasn't at all a bad job, and it gave me a chance of reading all sorts of books as well as studying music in my spare time. As soon as I could afford it I began having lessons from Isaac in Manchester--his real name's Isaacstein, but everybody calls him Isaac--I used to go once a week till he said he'd give me two lessons for the same money. He's really been awfully kind and generous, and he's quite a marvellous teacher. I wish you knew him. Well, all this has been going on now for some years; I've been improving my playing, I think, and I must admit I've been fairly happy all the time, only--only--" Her fluency ceased, and she gave him a queer abrupt smile across the table. "Only it isn't any longer enough to sat-isfy me. I could never get anyone to realise that, except Isaac. It's really not much use, is it, being fairly comfortable in what you're do-ing, if there's something else you want so dreadfully that you're willing to put up with all the discomforts in the world for it?"

"I know. I think I can understand that."

"That's how I feel about music. It's probably quite ridiculous of me, but I don't care--other people are constantly doing things which I think ridiculous."

"It's a difficult profession, of course."

"I know that. I'm prepared for all sorts of hardships, because I'm so certain in my own mind that they could never make me as un-happy as staying at home in Browdley. Besides, though it may seem a conceited thing to say, there is something in me. Musically, I mean. Even Isaac thinks there is. If I give myself a chance I might, some day, do something worth doing. Haven't you ever felt like that about any-thing?"

He did not answer, but said, instead: "What I'm rather puzzling over is why you didn't tell all this to your parents before you left. It seems such a pity to have needlessly quarrelled with them."

"But there was no quarrel--not on my side, at any rate. I told them I was going to live abroad, and I was quite ready and willing to give them the fullest details about it, but they wouldn't listen. I believe I did tell them a few things, but they obviously didn't believe me. When I saw it was no use talking to them any more, I just went to bed, packed up my things during the night, and caught the first train in the morning."

"Wasn't that rather precipitate?"

"What else could I have done? They wouldn't believe me or even listen. They never understood how I could be so keen on music, and I don't think they ever believed that when I went to Manchester so often in the evenings it was only for fiddle lessons. Recently, too, I've been doing most of my practising in Manchester, in a room belonging to a music-shop, because they didn't like the noise of it at home. Of course it is rather an awful noise sometimes, I admit."

"It seems a pity, though, that you couldn't have convinced them that it was all quite genuine."

"I often tried, I assure you. But in the end I just had to give up bothering. After all, if people *want* to think things of that sort..." She shrugged her shoulders and added: "I'm afraid you must think me very cool and ruthless about it. I dare-say you'd understand better if you knew my parents."

84

He said, more gently: "I do know them, a little. I can understand they were not very--sympathetic...Now tell me, what's given you this idea of going to Vienna?"

"I want to join a school there. Isaac says it's the best school in Europe, except one in Berlin, which I couldn't afford. Ail sorts of people attend the classes--men and women of all ages and from all countries. I have to pass a kind of entrance examination first of all, but Isaac says I'll do that quite easily."

"Has this Mr. Isaacstein--is that it?--has he been encouraging you in all these ideas?"

"No. He says, as you say, that it's a fearfully hard profession, and that I'm taking a big risk in giving up home and a job. But he likes my playing, all the same, and thinks there's about a hundred to one chance that I'll turn out pretty good."

"A hundred to one in your favour?"

'No, against me, of course."

"That doesn't sound very optimistic."

"He isn't optimistic, he just means everything he says."

"And, assuming he's correct, are you satisfied with such a chance?"

"I've got to be, haven't I? It's either that or no chance at all."

"What exactly will you do in this school?"

"Play the fiddle every day for hours and hours. Have lessons--perhaps from somebody of importance if I'm lucky. Eventually, if the hundred to one chance comes off, I'll begin giving recitals."

"Even that doesn't necessarily mean success. There are scores of recitalists one never hears of."

"Oh, I know. And you know, too, apparently. We both know." She laughed.

"I suppose you've carefully looked into the financial side of it all?"

"So carefully and so often that I know it by heart. I can live in Vienna--not luxuriously, of course, but then I wouldn't want to--on a hundred and fifty or so a year. Living's a little cheaper than it is in England. At the end of six months, if I show promise, the school may grant me a scholarship, and I might also be able to get a few outside pupils. I've saved up exactly a hundred and eighty-seven pounds during the past six years, so I can afford at least twelve months at the school, even as an experiment."

"What if the experiment doesn't succeed?"

"Then I'll at least know that I've had the chance and failed."

"You may find yourself back in England penniless and without a job."

"Possibly. But I'll manage somehow--I can typewrite and do shorthand, card-indexing, and all that sort of thing. I shan't need to go back to Browdley."

"It's taking a big plunge."

"I know."

"And you're not afraid of doing it?"

"I'm more afraid of not doing it. I'd be afraid of looking back when I'm older and wishing I'd had the nerve when I was young."

Howat rose abruptly from his chair, picking up the bill that the waitress had placed on the table. "Shall we go?" he said, smiling. "By the way, where are you staying in London?"

"With friends in South Kensington. Till to-morrow. I'm off in the morning."

"To Vienna?"

"Yes. It's the middle of term, but I think they'll probably let me begin. If not, I'll just wait there till next term."

He paid the bill downstairs and walked with her into the street. The crowds and traffic had not noticeably subsided in the interval. He reached the kerbside with her; they had neither of them spoken since leaving the shop; and he thought, as he stood there: Shall I say good-bye and wish her luck, or shall I continue an argument that hasn't the slightest chance of making her alter a single one of her intentions? Finally he adopted neither course, but said, altogether on impulse: "It just occurs to me that I'm feeling hungry. I haven't had anything to eat since my lunch on the train this morning. What about your own plans? Are you doing anything particular this evening?"

"There was a violin concert I wanted to go to."

"The one at the Cavendish?"

"That's it. How did you know?"

"I saw it advertised and rather thought of going myself."

"Then let's go together after we've had some food somewhere."

"That sounds a very happy suggestion."

"I know a place in Soho, quite good and not expensive."

"Splendid. We'll go there."

"It's near Regent Street. If you're hungry we'd better take a bus and go there now."

They crossed the road and waited for a Regent Street bus, but it was full inside and they had to climb to the roof, which was open to the sky and the cold wind. Yet something in that arctic elevation gave all Howat's perceptions a renewal of acuteness; once again he was caught up in swirls and eddies of enchantment, and as he felt her small tense body at his side, he knew that finding out the real truth about her had set a dizzying crown upon his happiness. She was pure and good; that was everything; and her purity merged with the new hopefulness of his own future into a single celestial harmony. He could not be quite sure how it all fitted in, but he felt, during that short tingling journey: There is nothing wrong with me, in the way I feared, and there is nothing wrong with her, in the way I feared. We are both all right, and the whole world is all right...and the more he thought about it, the more marvellous that simple discovery seemed to him. In the ever-changing pattern of lamplight he observed her profile, the delicate little chin cushioned serenely in the fur collar, the bold slope of the forehead under the close fitting hat--it was a pure profile, he thought, matching her in other ways, too--it looked so eager, intent, and not to be deflected. There was something in the way she stared ahead that put him in mind of a rather lovely figurehead of a ship.

But he still felt it somehow his duty to persuade her to return to Browdley, even though he knew the futility of the attempt. The Vienna idea seemed to him quite hopelessly impractical; even her friend Isaac had not been encouraging. Howat felt that he ought, at least, to stress the uncertainty of it, the risks of ultimate disappointment and failure. On the other hand, he reflected, she knew all the risks quite as well as he did; she was walking into them with her eyes open; and then, glancing towards her momentarily, he saw her as the living symbol of an attitude--that attitude of knowing and taking risks with eyes wide open. And it was an attitude which suddenly, by sheer loveliness of appeal, broke down his last misgiving, so that he said, there on that bus-top, just the opposite of what he felt he ought to say and just the essence of what he felt; he said, stooping a little to her: "My dear girl, I'm going to give you some advice which may rather surprise you. You go. Go to Vienna. Take your chance. Work hard, and may God be with you and reward your courage!"

She turned to him with a look of eager, startled friendliness, clutching his arm meanwhile like an excited child. "Thank you--thank you very much," she said simply, and he responded--"Oh, no, no--" and held her gloved fingers for a fraction of a moment in his cold hand. Her instant response to his benediction had filled him with overmastering ease of mind; he had done right, he was certain now, and he could even feel a touch of that priestly serenity he had so often imagined and envied. "But I *do* thank you," she insisted, and he could only repeat-"-Oh no, not at all..." His head was full of a divine singing, and all he could think of again was the astonishing rightness of himself, herself; and of all the world.

CHAPTER SEVEN - FRIDAY DINNER

She had said the Soho restaurant was not expensive; but it was, in fact, like most Soho restaurants, cheap if you picked out the very cheapest things, but fairly expensive to the person who asked for just what he wanted. Howat, sitting down at the small table and studying the bill of fare, did not feel in any mood to make intricate mathematical calculations. He was never very competent with money; if he had been alone he would doubtless have had eggs on toast in a Lyons shop for cheapness' sake; but, on the other hand, if Lyons had grossly overcharged him he would never have noticed it. So that, though he stared hard at the items on Barroli's comprehensive list, they conveyed little to his understanding--three and six for *poulet en casserole* seemed to him neither more nor less outrageous than a hundred pounds for a heating apparatus. Nor, apart from the prices, did he peruse very intelligently; he knew French, but to know French is not always to know the identities of dishes in a Soho restaurant owned by an Italian. Two things, however, supervened immensely above all his perceptions; he was hungry, and the world still retained its extraordinary attributes of perfection. As he gazed about he could not have conceived any restaurant pleasanter than the one whose interior surrounded him; he liked its touch of old-fashionedness, its red plush benches and baroque decorations; he liked the red-shaded table-lamp near his elbow, and the French and Italian newspapers on wooden frames that lay about; he liked the quick-moving and slightly shabby waiters, the smallness and easygoingness of the place, and the fact that at two tables nearest his own two different gentlemen were dining, the one, in full evening dress, with a lady, and the other, alone, in a very exuberant plus-fours.

In truth, it was just an average sort of place, better than some and not so good as others; its chief title to distinction, among a limited circle being an attractive kind of egg-nog made with sherry.

He said, across the table: "Remember now, this is a little farewell dinner in celebration of your Vienna adventure."

She smiled, and looking at her as she did so, he wondered how it had been possible for her to come to him for those lessons week after week without his noticing her more particularly. In the glow of the table-lamp he saw a rather pale oval face with a slender nose, longer than average, and a decidedly small mouth--like an Italian picture, he thought suddenly, and then, remembering the Raphael Saint Catherine, he said: "Oh, by the way, thanks for the picture you sent me. I liked it very much."

"I hoped you would. I felt I had to send you something, however trivial, in return for your kindness to me."

"*My* kindness to you?" As always, he was bewildered by the notion that he had ever been particularly kind to anybody.

"Yes, indeed," she answered, spiritedly. "You worked hard with my German, and you were always so patient. I did appreciate it, though I had an impression you didn't appreciate me. I rather came to the conclusion that I bored you."

"I'm sure you didn't do that."

"You always would keep so strictly to the subject--I so often wanted to have a real talk with you about other things, but you froze me up." She laughed. "How absurd it is to be telling you all this now!"

He laughed also. "It's rather odd as well as amusing, considering my daughter's opinion of me as a teacher. Sometimes, you know, I visit the school and take her class for a chance hour or so. She says I wander about from one subject to another in a most distracting way, that I never teach the children anything, and that I undermine her discipline by making them laugh too much."

"That sounds utterly delightful."

"Not from her point of view, though. She has to prepare them for examinations."

"Well, anyhow, I can't join her in complaining about you. You certainly taught me German all right and I don't think you made me laugh at all--not even once."

"Probably because I was being paid for the job. A sort of fundamental honesty urging me to give the utmost value for money."

They both laughed again, but in the background he was searching his memory for some clue to that earlier attitude; how was it, once again, that he had never noticed her particularly during those German lessons? He remembered how, when she had first approached him about giving them, he had wondered who she was, for the moment, and would have made some excuse for declining had she not revealed herself as his chapel secretary's daughter. Even after accepting, he had felt a little doubtful; he hadn't cared for the idea of giving private lessons to young girls...But the waiter's approach cut short such tangled recollections; it was more important now to decide what to eat.

A moment later, when the waiter had left them after taking the order, they intercepted each other's glances and smiled. "You're just thinking how extraordinary it is for you and me to be here, aren't you?" she asked.

"Yes, I was. But so many extraordinary things have been happening to me to-day. One of them, for instance, happened just before I met you. I went to see a specialist, thinking I might have something rather serious the matter with me, and he told me it was all nerves."

"Weren't you delighted?"

"Yes, altogether. I felt like a condemned prisoner who's been give a reprieve and a free pardon all at the same moment. I still feel rather like that. I left the doctor's place soon after a quarter to five, I suppose it was, and I hardly know what I did between then and seeing you. I remember getting into a taxi and being driven along Oxford Street. I never ride in taxis as a rule. For that matter, I never dine alone with young ladies in Soho restaurants. If I could see myself now from the outside, I daresay I should think I'd gone completely crazy."

"Having left the Euclid world and passed into the Einstein--that was your own simile, wasn't it?"

He looked across at her then with a curious, tranquil admiration. She was clever; she could seize a point; she had an alertness of mind that perfectly matched the alertness of her eyes and bearing. Trevis had the same kind of alertness, dimmed, though, by physical suffering; Ringwood had a touch of it, but in him it was rougher, less clarified. Only in her did this quality which he liked so much seem brought almost to perfection.

She went on: "I'm glad it was nothing seriously wrong. As a matter of fact, I had noticed you looking ill lately. I suppose you were worrying?"

"Yes, frightfully."

"I think you work far too hard in Browdley. Didn't the doctor tell you you had to take a rest?"

"I believe he did. D'you know, I hardly remember what he did tell me, except that I hadn't got what I thought I had. I believe he forbade me to speak in public again for a long time--it was my throat, you see, that was the bother--and I rather think he talked about a nervous breakdown. A breakdown! Do I look like it?"

"Not now, but you may when you get back to Browdley. I think you probably will. I don't know how you can ever stand the place. You must be so unhappy." She spoke that last word with a rather scared glance, as if it had arrived too impulsively to be checked.

"*Unhappy?*"

"Well, yes. Of course it's always difficult to imagine oneself in someone else's place, but I always feel--I always have felt--that if I were you I should be terribly unhappy."

"Unhappy!" he echoed again, but not interrogatively this time. He was so happy at that moment that the mere conception of being otherwise evaded him till, with a strong effort of imagination, he pictured Browdley, the Browdley he would be returning to on the morrow, its narrow streets of slums leading from the railway station to the Manse, the factory overshadowing the chapel, the little rooms in all the little houses that he visited.

"Because," she suggested, again with a scared glance, "because I feel that you try for so much, and must so often be disappointed."

He said: "Ah yes, but it isn't all disappointment, you know. And whether it is or not, I have to do it."

"You feel about it as I feel about music? That you must do it, whatever happens? You never have any doubts?"

"I don't think I ever had any when I was your age, anyhow. Perhaps when one reaches middle life, it isn't natural to be as certain of things."

"You have doubts, then?"

"Only of my own usefulness. It doesn't seem quite so inevitable that I shall convert the world as it did when I first left college."

"Do you want to convert the world?"

"I don't say I do--now. I'll be satisfied with doing a certain amount of good in Browdley."

"Giving up the big ambitions?"

"Don't you think doing a certain amount of good in Browdley is a big ambition? I do."

"Yes, so do I, but--" The waiter came with soup, and the interruption broke the sequence of discussion. "Really," she said afterwards, with a smile, "you must think I'm terribly impertinent, cross-examining you like this."

"Not so impertinent as I was to you a little while ago, I'm sure."

"Oh, *that?*" She laughed. "You don't mind my being amused by it, do you?"

"I'm relieved that you can be."

"Well, don't you think it was rather funny?"

"Perhaps..." And he laughed, with an effort at first, and then spontaneously.

"It was such an odd way of getting to know you," she went on. "I'd imagined all sorts of ways, but none in the least like that. Yes, I *had* imagined all sorts of ways. As a matter of fact, I'd been really wanting to know you ever since I heard you give an address on William Blake--two years ago, it must have been. Usually I hate literary talks, they're so artificial, and gushing, and speakers always quote the tags that you privately don't think much of--but you were different. You were rather queer, in a way. You talked totally above the heads of everybody in the audience (totally above my head, anyhow), and you went rambling on and on, about all sorts of things that had nothing to do with the subject--and yet somehow, in the end, I did get a vague idea of what you were driving at. Anyhow, I didn't come away feeling bored."

"So that was why, when you wanted to learn German--"

"Yes, precisely. I knew you knew the language, because I've seen you getting German books out of the library. But my parents didn't at all approve. To begin with, they couldn't see why I wanted to learn German at all, and then they said that since I never attended the chapel it was a piece of impudence for me to ask you."

"Oh, no, no, that never occurred to me." He paused a moment and then said: "By the way, as a mere matter of curiosity, why have you never attended the chapel?"

"Do you really want me to tell you?"

"Yes, very much."

She seemed to be having to arrange her thoughts. At length she replied: "I used to go regularly when I was younger. I was made to. It was the Silk Street chapel then, till my father had some kind of row with the minister there and decided to change to yours. I was seventeen and came to the conclusion that if he could please himself about which chapel he attended I ought to be able to please myself whether I attended one at all. There was a fuss about it at home, of course, but after all, at seventeen one can't exactly be dragged screaming along the aisle. And. I did go once or twice, just to sample it."

"And you didn't like it?"

"Not a very great deal. I never heard you preach, if that's any personal consolation."

"I'm afraid it isn't. What I really want to find out is your reason for disliking chapel itself."

"Well, to begin with, the building's not very attractive, is it? I wouldn't mind if it were downright ugly, like a factory, but it's got all those extra things on it--I don't know how to describe them--but it looks as if it had been built in a straightforward way by a builder and then someone had gone round sticking architecture on afterwards. Perhaps that's rather a vague criticism. As a matter of fact it reminds me too much of Gounod's music."

"You don't like Gounod?"

"No."

"Neither do I, particularly. And I quite agree with all that you say about the chapel building; it's the product of a period when taste in architecture was at its lowest. Still, that alone oughtn't to keep anyone outside."

"Oh no, it wouldn't keep me, either, if I liked everything else. But I suppose I don't."

"Tell me, if you can, some of the other things that you don't like."

"Well, there's the organ, and the way the organist plays it, and the hymns--such stupid words, very often, which people sing without meaning them--'False and full of sin I am', for instance--do you think anyone in your chapel really thinks he's false and full of sin? I'm quite sure my father doesn't. Nor do the rest, either--they're far too proud of being respectable middle-class people ever to have such a thought...And the tunes are sometimes rather dreadful, too."

"I'll even agree with you in most of all that. I did try years ago to improve the music, but it led to trouble with the organist and choirmaster; they said I was interfering outside my province. Probably I was. It isn't an easy job, you know, being a parson."

"I'm sure it isn't. That's why I said just now I was sorry for you--you must find so many things that seem all wrong."

"Most of us have that experience, don't we? But tell me now, apart from the building and the music, which we both agree are far from perfect, what is it that you really dislike? I'm certain it can't be entirely a matter of externals."

"It isn't, but it's rather difficult to answer without being impolite."

"Oh, I shan't be offended--I asked for it, and anyhow, I really do want to know."

She replied, musingly and with evident care: "I think it's probably that I don't feel sympathy with the spirit of the place. It all seems rather bleak to me, and it doesn't seem to have much room for art and beauty--in a way, I feel it almost distrusts that sort of thing. I know I can't prove what I'm saying--I'm only telling you just how things appear to me. And the revivals you sometimes have--they're a bit hysterical--and I'm not built to like that sort of business. And then the preaching--I don't care much for the system that encourages practically anybody to preach. I can't feel interested, somehow, in what all kinds of people tell me, out of their own heads, so to speak, about religion."

"There, of course, you attack the whole foundation of Nonconformity--perhaps even of Protestantism altogether."

"Do I? I'm not really trying to attack anything--I'm only describing a few rather shadowy feelings I have."

"Quite. I see that." On any other occasion he would have felt immensely worried and perturbed and would have been bursting with eloquent confutations and counter-arguments; but with her, rather oddly, he felt no inclination to do anything but just go on talking quietly and discovering her opinions on one thing after another. It was queer how comfortable he felt, and how pleasantly in sympathy with her, even all the time that she was undermining, in a few calm sentences, the whole fabric of his professional existence; the truth was that beyond and surpassing any disagreement with her ideas was an extraordinary interest in them that had taken possession of him.

The waiter here provided a second interruption by removing the soup-plates and bringing a large *Sole Colbert* on a dish; it looked so enormous, even when divided, that they broke off their religious argument to discuss the more urgent if less exalted matter of appetite. "I'm astonished to find how hungry I am," he declared, zestfully. "I never fed equal to this sort of thing at home. It must be the change of air."

"More likely the good cooking," she answered, and then, perceiving the implication of her remark, flushed slightly. "Really, I'm saying the most dreadful things; I don't know why it is; I just seem to find myself speaking to you exactly as I feel--anything that comes into my head...But I think it's true, though, about the cooking. Once, when I came to your house for a German lesson, you were out, and the maid had me in the kitchen talking to her. She was alone there, cooking your dinner, I suppose, and ever since watching her that morning, I've had an extra reason for being sorry for you."

He laughed. "I never trouble about food when I'm at home. I don't think I'm really very interested in it. Of course, it's different to-night, but then, to-night..."

The waiter approached with the wine-list, and Howat, after a moment's hesitation, passed it across the table to her. "Will you choose something you like?" he asked, doubtfully.

She also was doubtful. "I'm afraid I'm very ignorant about drinks. I'd rather you ask for something *you* would like."

"Something *I'd* like?" He was about to disclaim any desire for non-teetotal drink of any kind when suddenly an impulse seized him and he began talking, almost to himself: "I remember something I once had--I was in Germany, on a holiday, as a youth--it was some kind of beer, I think--ah, here's the list--I wonder if I shall call to mind the name..." He glanced down the column and felt a slight stirring of memory. "Ah, Pilsener, Pilsener--that was it. Yes, I think I'd like to drink it again, after all these years. But what about you? Won't you have wine?"

"I'll have the beer with you. May I?"

"All right." And he gave the order to the waiter, who had probably never before heard Pilsener discussed with such solemnity.

But when the waiter had gone she laughed. "I think that's rather a symbolic act," she said. "Wouldn't Browdley be shocked?"

"Possibly. But without reason. It's merely another instance of the quite exceptional things that can happen during an Einstein inter-lude." He smiled buoyantly, yet a moment later, after watching the pale brown liquid stream into the glasses, he took up his own with a certain sense of significance. It was true, of course, that this simple glass of beer was quite sufficient to shatter all kinds of reputations that he possessed in Browdley; but somehow he could not bring himself to be concerned about it. The cool drink, slightly iced, gave him far dif-ferent thoughts, breaking through the years till he remembered himself, a young man in his early twenties, on that first thrilling holi-day abroad, walking along a winding Rhenish lane amidst blazing sunlight, and calling for a drink at a little wayside refreshment-house where he had sat outside at a bare scrubbed table with a group of working men in peaked caps. He had asked for mineral water, but the girl, misunderstanding his German, had brought him a mug of some-thing which he drank and enjoyed before he realised that it was actually that horrible and dreaded infamy--beer.

He told this story now and she was highly amused, and they went on talking gaily, yet with certain intervals of seriousness, throughout the rest of the meal, until the black coffee, accompanied with cigarettes, provided just that epilogue of reflectiveness that pre-pared them for the next stage of the evening's progress. The concert was timed to begin at eight, and at seven thirty he called for the bill and paid a sum which, if he had ever thought about it (but he did not), would have seemed entirely fantastic.

On the pavement outside the restaurant someone said "Taxi, sir?" and he answered "Yes" in the same mood of impulsiveness that had made him ask for Pilsener.

CHAPTER EIGHT - FRIDAY EVENING

In the taxi he began to wonder what was really happening, and after musing for a time a word occurred to him, a rather astonishing word, he thought, but so definitely the right one that he did not seek for any other. It was all a 'lark'. It was quite the most gigantic lark he had ever had; but then, in fact, his life up to the present had been somewhat deficient in larks of any kind. And it was good for him, he felt, or at any rate, not bad for him, to indulge in such an occasional escapade. Dinner, talk, music--what could be more harmless? After all, he reflected, he had something to celebrate as well as she.

Besides, like all the best larks--perhaps it was what made them the best--it was all to be such a transient thing. To-morrow she would be abroad, to-morrow he would be in Browdley, and possibly, indeed probably, they would never see each other again. She would have those hours and hours of fiddle practice that she longed for, and he would be back in his little world of guild meetings and chapel services, good works and bad cooking. He saw, with a certain grim relish, the years stretching ahead of him; viewed in mind from the dark recesses of a taxi after a good dinner they seemed to reflect, mirror-like, something of that queer quality in the present-which could only be indicated by that same word--a. 'lark'. After all, the spirit of fun, of adventure, of enterprise, was surely not to be confined to a single place or occasion. Why should there not be adventure in Browdley? He felt, with conviction, that he would be all the better for this London 'night-out' when he got home; it had been a revelation of something he had so far rather missed--the joy of life, that unreasonable and illogical human joy that made a man buy what he could not afford and drink (for once) against his convictions and progress to sudden enchanting intimacy with someone whose very charm, perhaps, lay partly in the unlikelihood of any further meeting.

He looked out of the cab-window and glimpsed again the throbbing and incredibly lovely world--the omnibuses and taxis and private cars passing by with people in them he would never know, each with a life-history, ambitions, and a soul to be saved; the whole pageant of life, no more real of course than was to be seen in Browdley, yet somehow swifter, more picturesque in its setting of electric sky-signs and opera-cloaks. He felt like an explorer, almost, in a strange land; all this goes on, he thought, night after night, just as night after night in Browdley the factory-sirens scream at half-past five and the crowds come tumbling into the streets--the curious, animated routine of two worlds, each ignorant of the other, and meeting, when they did, only in the gaze of some bewildered intermediary like himself. He thought of how such a contrast would strike Councillor Higgs, how it would all seem to him no more than a demonstrated theorem from the economics text-book; which might be very sound and scientific, but now Howat was perceiving another aspect--there was this question of joy, of 'having a lark', in which, despite Councillor Higgs, the poor were altogether in agreement with the rich. Both understood perfectly the technique of 'the good time', and both were looked at askance by the intermediate class. That made him think of the girl's description of his Browdley congregation--'respectable middle-class people', she had called them, and it was accurate enough; he tried in vain to call to mind a single 'chapel' family that did not come easily within the category. Some were hard up, he knew, but all were of the class that could sniff superiorly in both directions. Why was it that none of the really poorest and commonest people ever came to his chapel? He had seen them often enough outside the Catholic church. Was it possible, he thought, with an uprush of indignation, that he had been doing nothing for a dozen years but preach to the already converted? Suppose for the future he were to concentrate on the rest? But what had he to offer them? Respectability? The right hand of fellowship as dispensed by a narrow-minded and tight-fisted shopkeeper? A Letitia Monks Vestry complete with sham-Gothic gargoyles? Sermons about the Christian life by one who had passed the age of forty without knowing much about any kind of life?

She interrupted his stormy self-questionings to ask what it was that had kept him silent for half the length of Regent Street.

"Rather an odd thought," he answered. "It just occurred to me that if ever there's armed revolution in this country I daresay I shall escape, if I wear my collar, and I wouldn't be surprised if those fellows in opera-hats over there escape too, but the gutters will probably be running with the blood of respectable middle-class people who go to chapel."

"That sounds rather fierce."

"Yes, perhaps I don't mean it very seriously. But I feel fierce enough when I call to mind all the lies that were told me about you.

"Oh, don't bother about them. Why do you care any more than I do what people say?"

"You really don't care, do you?"

"Not a bit."

Accidentally in the darkness of the cab his hand touched hers, and the contact, together with her answer, gave him a suddenly warming affection for her, and through her, for all struggling and adventurous humanity--for the street urchin fighting his first fight, for the speculator staking a fortune on some hairline of probability, for the artist never quite succeeding, and for all kinds of obvious heroes and heroines as well; he saw her spirit in them all, and that such a spirit should be maligned by the secure and the unadventurous swept him again into passionate indignation.

But they had reached the concert-hall and the uniformed commissionaire was holding open the taxi-door.

As soon as he was settled comfortably in his seat he wanted to laugh. He felt so happy, and he had been anticipating this moment of settlement for so long, and the people all around him looked so very solemn, and the girl at his side stared ahead with such radiant eagerness at the sleek grand piano on the platform. The Cavendish was one of the older concert halls, and gazing round at its chocolate and gold decorations he said: "This is nearly as ugly as my chapel, isn't it?"--"Rather uglier, if anything, I think," she replied, and the retort pleased him obscurely and made him want to laugh more than ever.

But soon they found something definitely merrymaking, for the printed programme contained a series of verbal descriptions and interpretations of the music, such as--"Now all the noontide rapture and pulsating vitality of the preceding movement have given place to a calm twilight atmosphere in which the soul begins to glimmer like a star"; and they made the sudden mutual discovery that this was the sort of thing that amused them both intensely. For the next few minutes it seemed a pity to do anything but rummage through their programmes with occasional remarks of "Oh, *do* read this--it's better still!"--until they became so uproarious that people near them began to look round reprovingly. "Really," he exclaimed at last, after laughing a great deal, "is this a proper mood for approaching great music?"--and she answered: "Yes, I think it is--much better, anyhow, than the mood of the person who wrote that programme stuff." He responded: "Yes, yes--oh, yes," with almost worshipful eagerness; he knew what she meant, and it was somehow deep with all kinds of meanings that were his also.

"It would be much more intelligent to call music just a nice noise, as a child might," she said.

"I agree. These attempts to describe tunes in words are ridiculous. You can't ever be sure what a composer means."

"Why should he mean anything at all? Isn't the nice noise that he invents reason enough?"

"Reason enough for us, but is it *his* reason? Why does he compose?"

"Because he feels like it, or because it's his job. Or, most often perhaps, because he can't help it."

"The person who wrote these programme notes would think your reasons very unromantic."

"I think they're tremendous reasons. Especially to do something because you can't help doing it."

"Yes, I think I've had that feeling myself at odd times."

"When you first became a minister, I suppose?"

He seemed puzzled for a moment. "No doubt," he replied at length. "But that wasn't really in my mind. I was thinking of once or twice when *I've* tackled music composition."

"You've composed?" she queried, her eyes showing more surprise than her words.

"Only a little. When I was younger I was very keen."

"What did you compose?"

"Songs, hymn-tunes, all sorts of things. I once won ten pounds for a string quartet. That was my biggest hit."

"Where was that?"

"At a musical festival in East London. I had the pleasure of hearing my quartet played once, very badly, at a special festival concert; that was twenty odd years ago, and I'm fairly certain it's never been heard anywhere since."

"It must have been pretty good."

"It wasn't bad, I admit. But it wasn't very good, either. I won the prize because the others were worse."

"I'd like to know more about it. I never guessed you'd done that sort of thing."

"Well, I never guessed you were interested in music at all."

"I know. It was a pity."

And while he was pondering on what exactly she meant or could mean by that, the pianist and violinist appeared on the platform and the audience broke into applause. The first item was the Kreutzer Sonata, and from the very opening notes Howat had the impression of never having heard it, or even any music, before. He was amazed and a little awed by the feeling; it was terrifying, this acuteness of perception that had come over him--something beyond his mastery, threatening to engulf him in a flood of turbulent sensation, and though he could not identify it with anything known or imagined, yet during the Andante movement it rose in him to such a curious ache that but for the girl at his side and the thought of making a disturbance he might have left the hall. He gripped with his hands tightly on the arm-rests and commanded himself not to be so foolish, so overcome; it was absurd that even music should create such emotional tumult; but it was not the music alone, he explained to himself, but the strange sequence of events that had been happening all day. To-morrow, anyhow, he reflected, would see him reduced to his normal temperature; to-morrow, walking down the slope at Browdley Station, he would step into his old accustomed groove. But the final presto movement swept him out of all such reassurance into a world in which even thought could not be resolved into words, or even feeling into thought. Only the applause at the finish wakened him to reality. He felt dazed, then, and exhausted, as if he had been fighting some secret battle all alone.

The girl, fresh and confidant, turned to him immediately. They discussed the Kreutzer performance for a time, and then she wanted to know more, in detail, about composing work. He told her, as well as he could, and she listened with grave attention. "Why don't you do any of it now?" she asked, afterwards.

"I do, occasionally. I put in an hour or two only this last week--trying a song for the school Christmas concert."

"But you've given up your big ambitions?"

"Oh, entirely."

"Is it because you don't think any more that you *could* do anything big? Don't you think it's in you to do it?"

He pondered and replied slowly: "Honestly, I don't know for certain, but I should say probably not. I was far too ambitious years ago, that's obvious. Of course I have a certain amount of talent--it could perhaps be developed if I had the time. But I haven't the time, and never will have, so really it's not much use thinking about it, is it?"

"I believe," she said, thoughtfully, "that these things usually work themselves out in the right way. I mean, if there is great stuff in anyone, it *does* come out--it *has* to--nothing else can happen. One would just give up everything for it. The same old reason--doing something because you can't help doing it."

He smiled. "Very well, when you hear that I've given up my pastorate in Browdley to go and compose string quartets in some garret in Chelsea, or wherever they do compose them, you can assume that I've done it because I couldn't help doing it."

The programme then continued. The pianist played a Schumann group; next followed the Brahms A Major Piano and Violin Sonata.

101

Howat had hoped all along that they would play this, and its name on the programme had set a further seal upon the perfection of the evening. Now, as it began, he fell into a second storm of emotion, but he did not, as during the Kreutzer, attempt resistance; he let himself be carried along the crest of the flood-tide and, at the end, found himself tranquil, though in a strange harbour. He could not collect his thoughts for a time, but it was the end of the concert and people were already chattering and shuffling out of their seats. He rose with his companion and joined the crowd streaming to the exits; "I like that Brahms," he said, soberly; and she answered: "So do I." There came a point in experience, he reflected (and he felt that she realised it also), when understatement was the less absurd of alternatives. When they were halfway to the doors renewed applause brought on the performers again; they played a short encore piece--some little modern thing which Howat did not know and did not particularly care for either. Nor did she; and he thought: How I like that way she has of being so effortlessly cool and downright--the way she says 'I like this' or 'I don't care .for that'--with her eyes clear as crystal and her nose in the air like some high-spirited thoroughbred. But there was something warm and excited behind the crystal coolness, and in the lobby outside the hall she suddenly took his arm and exclaimed: "I don't want to go in yet--it's quite early. Are you tired? Do you want to go back to your hotel?"

He had never thought about the matter until now, but he answered: "Oh no, I'm not tired, either."

"I'm afraid it's selfish of me--I'm forgetting the long day you've had."

"I've had one of the most extraordinary days of my life--far too wonderful to have been tiring."

"You'll be tired to-morrow."

"I shall probably sleep in the train all the way.

"Then at Browdley I suppose your work begins again immediately?"

"Yes. I've got a Bazaar Committee meeting and the Young Men's class to-morrow night, and Sunday's going to be even busier than usual, because it's Armistice Day."

"And I shall be on my way to Vienna. Isn't it odd to think about it? Do you suppose we shall ever meet again?"

"If you come to Browdley, perhaps, or if I go to Vienna."

"Neither of which seems very likely, does it?"

"I'm afraid it doesn't."

"Then we've got to make the most of what's left. When I think of all those hours we spent over the German without ever guessing how much we both liked--Brahms--"

"I once heard you humming the opening theme of that sonata. I was rather surprised."

"There was your chance. If you had only asked me about it--"

"I know. I wish I had asked you. I'm an awful misser of chances."

"Does nobody in Browdley know *anything* about you?"

"Oh, I'm not really such a mystery as all that. I think quite a number of people know me fairly well."

"But the music?"

"That's not a secret--it's merely that most people aren't interested. You wouldn't be, unless you were keen on the thing yourself."

They had walked away from the hall and were now in quiet and almost deserted side-streets. "Where shall we go?" she asked, and he could not give any definite answer, except a suggestion that they should make their way nearer to the theatres and restaurants. He knew little about London's night civilisation and at that moment cared even less. His senses were full of enchantments, and he was perfectly happy to be strolling in a direction which, by instinct rather than calculation, he believed to be correct. With her arm in his they walked all the way, skirting spacious squares and across the main traffic highways and into narrow yards and alleys and diagonally across short streets from lamp-post to lamp-post, past shuttered windows and cabmen's shelters and cats sitting delicately in doorways; till at last a distant glow over roofs came so near that they walked abruptly right into it--it was Piccadilly Circus. All the way they had been talking, but now they stopped, dazzled by the brilliance, and felt for a moment like country cousins. There were so many restaurants where evening dress was clearly expected, and so many others whose precise character did not look too obvious, that finally Howat made for the swing doors of the Regent Palace Hotel; he had heard of it; it was where people from Browdley sometimes stayed.

Under the dome in the lounge of that rather amazing establishment they took coffee and sandwiches and smoked cigarettes. A certain recklessness was on him, not diminished by the realisation that it was approaching an hour when all good parsons are in bed. The colourful scene alternately attracted and repelled; it pulsated with crude, animal vitality, and the saxophones droning in the distance expressed that vitality to perfection, within the limits of their own peculiar technique. It was all something that he rather disliked, yet it drew him nearer in mind and sympathy to the girl at his side; he looked at her as she sat there, so calm and close to him, and he thought: But for you I should be fantastically unhappy in this place, but with you it's rather exhilarating; you make its vitality stand out; you're like a prism, through which I'm managing to see all kinds of different, magical things...And then, in a way that had never happened before, he reflected: Browdley--Browdley--Browdley to-morrow...

"I hope we *shall* meet again sometime," he said, transmuting his thought a little.

"Yes, I do, too," she answered, and they exchanged a glance that lasted only a fraction of a second, and then went on talking, about music and pictures and books and all kinds of side-topics that thrust themselves unwanted yet unshirked into the conversation; it was midnight before they decided that they really must go. As they passed through the crowded lobby and into the street, he said: "Let me see now--where is it you said you were staying?"

"South Kensington. It's a studio in a sort of mews. The people who have it are rather amusing--the man's an actor and the woman paints--very badly, I'm afraid--but they've both been awfully nice to me. They're friends of Isaac's, and when he wrote to them about me they asked me to stay with them as long as I was in London."

Crowds were jostling down the tube entrances.

"I suppose the tube's your best way," he said, "but there seems a tremendous rush. Would you rather try for a bus? It's not so quick, but usually pleasanter."

"I've got a return ticket from Charing Cross. That's only a few minutes' walk away."

So they set off down the Haymarket and across Trafalgar Square; six-and-a-half hours, he reflected, since he had met her there outside the post office; but the interval was hardly reckonable in time. Down Northumberland Avenue to the river the wind swept past them in cold gusts; little pools in the gutters were already frozen hard. They crossed the tramlines to look at the river, rolling by like coils of black snakes; the railway bridge soared above them, glittering with red and green signal-lights. A moving brilliance zoomed across and sent a cascade of silver-blue sparks into the darkness below. "How beautiful that is," she exclaimed, watching the train disappear over the south side.

"That's the bridge they're always talking of pulling down because they say it's ugly and spoils what's supposed to be one of the finest views in the world."

"I think it's much more beautiful than a good many views of that sort."

104

"Yes. It represents the best of its period just as the architecture of my chapel represents the worst. The Victorians only achieved beauty when they aimed at utility."

"I know. I always think the best things in Browdley to show visitors are the cotton-mills. They're so downright ugly you can stand them--they're almost beautiful because of that. Anyhow, they're not depressing, and they don't put on airs, like the Town Hall and the Technical School."

They walked over the road to the station entrance and he was full of the feeling that there were unnumbered things he wanted to say to her and that as soon as she was gone they would all come tumbling upon him. But when they reached the booking-hall they found there were no more trains. They might get a bus, someone suggested, in the Strand, so they hurried back along Northumberland Avenue to Trafalgar Square and puzzled themselves over several vehicles, all quite full, that were bound for places neither of them had ever heard of. At length he said: "Well, we can walk a little way, unless you're tired, and get one as it overtakes us. I daresay there'll be room in them soon." It sounded rather vague, but she agreed without argument, and they skirted the corner of the square and passed under the Admiralty Arch into the Mall, unaware that omnibuses did not traverse that spacious highway. But it was pleasant enough to stroll at one o'clock in the morning under the leafless trees. At last a turning opened out on the left and she exclaimed: "Oh, let's go down here, it leads through St. James's Park to Victoria Station--I know there are always late buses from there. And there's no hurry so far as I'm concerned; those people I'm with always stay up half the night. Besides, they gave me a key."

They entered the park. He was not quite sure how it would help the journey to South Kensington, but he was still in rather the mood of not caring--after all, it was their last chance, they would never meet and talk again. The prospect of that imminent farewell gave him not so much a feeling of sadness as of something cold and rather blank that he must soon encounter and become used to. He wondered, then, for the first time, if they would correspond. On the whole, he thought better not; there could be no particular point in it, since they would probably never renew the acquaintance. But he did say, with a fervour that rather astonished him: "When you're in Vienna I don't suppose you'll think a great deal about Browdley--no reason, of course, why you should--but I do want you to feel that--in any emergency--you have a friend there. Remember now. At any time--years hence, perhaps--a letter to me will not be wasted. I mean, I shall always want to help you, if it should ever happen that I can. And I daresay I shall always be in Browdley, so you'll know where to write."

She said: "It's very kind of you, and I do thank you. I shall like to feel that. I wish there'd been more time for us to get to know each other. It's absurd, really--dashing away like this to the opposite ends of the earth. They are rather opposite ends, aren't they?"

"Absolutely, I should say."

"And it's so lovely here to-night. What's that building over there with all the lights shining on it?"

"I don't know. I don't think I really know where I am."

"Probably I'm dragging you miles out of your way. I keep forgetting how tired you must be. What time's your train to-morrow?"

"There's one at ten-thirty I might try for."

"Mine's at ten."

"I suppose we both ought to hurry up and get some sleep."

"I won't sleep. I'll be too excited."

"About to-morrow?"

"Yes. And to-day."

He felt the very slightest pressure of her arm in his, and the sensation moved him to a curious whimsical tenderness. "Elizabeth," he said (he had never called her by her name until then)--"to-day *has* been rather fine, hasn't it? Finer, for me, probably, than for you. It seems a hundred years since a solitary grey-haired parson stepped out of a train at St. Pancras Station and carried his bag to a second-rate hotel in Bloomsbury. He was tired and worried, partly because he thought he was very ill, and partly because he had to face an embarrassing interview with a certain young lady of whom he had not had, to be candid, the very best reports."

He had expected her to be amused, but instead she was silent for a time and then responded, as if with some effort to achieve the same mood: "But you're not solitary and I don't think you're really very grey-haired, either. Besides, even if you were both, the description wouldn't do, because it suggests someone old and decrepit. You aren't exactly that, are you, Howat? Is 'Howat' what I have to call you? It's a queer name, isn't it?"

"It was my father's. I think it suits a parson, though *he* wasn't one--it has just a slight flavour of pretentiousness. I sometimes wish I had another name. No, no, I don't--I really don't care at all. I'm not sure that I know what I'm talking about."

"Perhaps that's why you called yourself solitary."

"More likely I was thinking of those old-fashioned boys' yarns in magazines years ago that used to begin--'One glorious summer's evening, in the heart of the Canadian Rockies, a solitary horseman might have been seen--'"

"I don't think you do know what you're talking about."

"Of course not. I warn you, I shall talk nothing but nonsense till we say good-bye."

He felt, indeed, as if a divine yet rather wistful nonsense were closing round him on all sides. The sky was full of stars and there was a new moon, and that shining building, whatever it was, now stood directly ahead, its tall square tower, brilliantly flood-lit, facing them like some fairy goal beyond the trees. The path they were traversing sloped gently down to the suspension bridge over the ornamental water, and there the loveliness of the scene was like a sudden droning in his ears; he stopped, and put his arm round her shoulder as they both gazed down at the water and then across to the spectral buildings in the distance. "There's the Foreign Office, I think," she said, and he replied: "Ah yes, yes..." But he was thinking of something else; he was thinking--By God, I believe there is something in me, if it had a chance; I believe what I'm everlastingly seeking for wouldn't always elude...He felt as if some utmost beauty of the world were calling to him with open arms, while he, for some unfathomable reason, wanted to answer yet could not either speak nor stir.

When, a few moments later, they entered Bird-cage Walk, Big Ben was chiming the quarter, and it was too late, he guessed, to think of finding an omnibus. He asked for the address where she was staying and summoned the first taxi that carne along. He would accompany her, he planned, say good-bye at her destination, and return to his hotel in the same taxi.

As they drove off she said: "Don't go back straight away. Can't you spare a minute to come up and see the people I'm staying with? I think you'll probably like them--they're interesting."

"Isn't it rather late for paying a call?"

"Oh, they don't care. They very often stay up most of the night talking to people. And they've got a photograph of Isaac--I'd rather like you to see it."

"Yes, 'I'd like to myself. All right, I'll come, but I really mustn't stay long. Think of my train to-morrow."

"And mine. Just now I find them both rather dreadful to think of."

"Ah, but you'll love Vienna."

"Have you been there?"

"No, but I've always had a great desire to go. Not that I ever will--it's too far. The Viennese are supposed to be delightful people."

"So long as Viennese landladies don't object to fiddle practice."

"Perhaps some day I shall pay my five-and-ninepence to hear that fiddle."

"I should think it very, very improbable."

"You don't know."

"In a way I don't care. As I told you, I'm not especially optimistic about making money and being successful. I'm just doing everything because I must--because I don't seem to be able to get what I want any other way. It's a personal thing. I don't really care a bit about showing off before other people, though I'd be willing enough to do it for a living. I just want to play the fiddle, that's all."

"I think I understand."

"I really believe you do, and I'm certain nobody else does."

"Except Isaac?"

"Ah yes, except him." They both laughed. "You'll like his face, I think. He's terribly ugly, so people say, but I never noticed it particularly."

"He has understanding, anyhow."

"Yes. He knows how it is that so many things don't matter when once you're certain what does matter. At his cinema, for instance, he has to play the most awful music from three every afternoon until eleven at night, but he doesn't mind. He says very often he doesn't even *hear* it."

"I can believe that. Often I don't hear my own congregation singing a very bad hymn tune half a semitone flat. I suppose I've got used to it."

"Isn't that a pity, though, in your case? You'd have hated it at one time, wouldn't you?"

"Yes, I did hate it, then."

"And nowadays you don't bother?"

"I try not to. Somehow, though it perhaps sounds foolish to say so, I'm a bit afraid of bothering. It would be so easy for me to bother too much."

"You weren't afraid years ago."

"Oh, heavens, no. I was keen enough till--oh, till I realised it wasn't much use being keen. When I was in my teens and early twenties I used to scribble down tunes nearly every night. My parents died when I was young, and I went to live with a rather fine old dissenting preacher in a small Kentish village. There was a family of seven daughters. I remember some of them used to sing--the usual kind of songs people did sing in those days--and I sometimes tried to teach them things of my own, but it was never much of a success. I'm sure the fault was chiefly mine--they were probably written in impossible keys. It was the youngest girl, by the way, who afterwards became my wife."

"Were you very much in love with her?"

The question, so artless and direct, took him by surprise, so far as anything, in the mood he was in, could have done so; he reflected for a second and then evaded with: "Don't you think people who marry are usually in love at the time?"

"At the time? Do you mean only that?"

He felt her keen, eager mind in sharp contact with his own; it was exciting and a little uncanny, the way she could open up long avenues of speculation, not so much by her questions as by the questions that her questions suggested. He did not know what to say in answer, but the taxi rescued him from the problem by drawing in and halting at the kerbside. He paid the driver and then, as the cab drove away, stared around with a renewed sense of strangeness; there they were, the two of them, marooned at that rather forlorn hour of the morning amidst a waste of empty pavements and tall unlit houses. "This way," she said, leading him into a narrow side turning that appeared to expand further on into a sort of enclosed yard. "These used to be stables belonging to those big houses, but now they're mostly garages. My friends are lucky because the garage they live over belongs to a man who spends half the year abroad. They're really quite comfortable places to live in. This way. I suppose as it's so late I'd better use the key."

She took a Yale key from her bag and unlocked a door that gave directly on to the yard. A dark interior was revealed, and a second later, when she had switched on the light, a small lobby with a flight of stairs ascending to a first floor. "We'll go up," she said, "they're probably in the studio." She climbed the stairs, with Howat following her. All this seemed to be happening, so far as he was aware, in a curious dream, a dream in which the most fantastic things followed one another with a kind of preposterous reasonableness. At the top of the stairs was a landing with several closed doors; she opened one of them, switched on a light, and gazed around. The room was empty, but it bore signs of having been fairly recently inhabited. Used glasses stood on a Sheraton sideboard, and there was a cabinet gramophone with a record still on the turntable. It was a rather cosily furnished room, in which one window had evidently been enlarged to give a good north light. There were several bookcases, a baby grand piano, and an easel supporting a half finished and not very attractive portrait of a ballet-dancer.

"They don't seem here," she said, and then caught sight of a letter on the mantelpiece addressed, in a very conspicuous scribble, to herself. She tore open the envelope and a few seconds later exclaimed: "They've gone away for the week-end--some friends called and invited them suddenly." She handed Howat the note; it was signed 'Finola', and in the course of a few dozen roughly pencilled words conveyed an explanation, an apology, good wishes for the future, a hope that she would be sure to come again when next she was in London, and a command for her to make herself thoroughly comfortable during that last night at the studio. "That's Finola," she added, and pointed to a portrait on the wall of a pale thin-lipped woman with prominent cheek bones and a necklace of large green beads. "She painted that of herself, but it doesn't flatter. I'm sorry you couldn't have met her--and her husband. But its really just like them to go rushing off in such a hurry."

"I'm sorry, too. I like their room. It's got a sort of genial untidiness about it."

"They're like that themselves--genial and untidy. I'm very fond of them both, though I've only known them for a few days. It's queer how a room can sometimes make you feel at home, isn't it?"

"Yes, this one does, I admit. It's the casualness of it--everything just comfortably anyhow."

"They *are* casual--the way they just go off at a moment's notice like this, for instance. Somehow I don't feel it's at all impolite of them."

"No, it's almost a charming characteristic. This room makes me wish my own wasn't so stiff and formal. But I'm afraid that's in the hands of my sister-in-law. She has the strictest ideas about tidying up. I can just imagine how shocked she'd be by a place like this."

"Yes, I know. I met her once. I found her just a bit terrifying."

"She's very good-hearted, of course. I don't know what my wife would do without her, with all that great house to look after."

"Why don't you move into a smaller house?"

"I think that's what I would do if I had my own way."

"I'm sure you'd be happier."

"Yes...Those enormous houses were part of a different social system altogether. I'd be just as comfortable and certainly much better off living over a garage. After all, what does it matter where you live?"

"Provided you're happy in what you're doing...I like that picture over there, don't you? They picked it up at a sale the other day--they're always picking things up. That's why the place is in such a glorious muddle. I don't believe they ever 'furnished', as people say. I imagine they just began with an almost empty room and let things accumulate."

"Not a bad way. Better than going to a shop and buying vanloads of standardised stuff all at once."

She was leaning against the mantelpiece with her heels on the fender-rail when suddenly she slipped and caused a little clatter of fire-irons. The noise awoke him from the almost trance-like gossip in which he had been taking part; it was as if both of them, more or less unconsciously, had been talking hard to obscure the fact that they were alone in someone else's studio at half-past one in the morning, and would soon be saying good-bye, never to meet again.

He looked at his watch. "Really, I ought to go. It's very late."

"Yes, I suppose it is...Oh, you haven't seen that photograph of Isaac. It's in their other room--I'll get it for you."

She rushed away and reappeared a few seconds later with a cabinet-sized photograph of a rather fleshy, genial-looking man, obviously a Jew, with a high domed forehead and deep-set eyes that more than made up for coarse features in the lower part of the face. Howat studied it closely and with a certain willingness to be impressed. "Yes, he's an interesting-looking man," he said at length.

She was standing near him, gazing over his arm at the photograph. "He--he's a musician," she responded, with a sudden stammer in her voice.

I know--I can believe ii. He felt a warm spring of sympathy rising in him, and beyond it, a tinge of whimsical envy; the girl, he realised, was fond of this man in a way which it was not given to many men to experience; and he had a vague sensation of desire, of desire to share the rays of such eager, comradely affection. He felt, amidst the flurry of that desire--I wish she were my daughter; and then he thought of his own daughter, cramming away at her text-books, and rejecting all in life that did not assist in her melancholy progress from matriculation to 'inter' and from 'inter' to 'final'; he thought, dispassionately: Mary's a rather unattractive girl, she'll probably never marry, it's just as well she is keen on degrees and things. Yet why, be reflected, was there such a tremendous difference, between his own daughter's ambitions and this girl's musical career in Vienna, between his daughter's Latin verbs and the German lessons he had given to Elizabeth Garland? He felt that there *was* a difference, absolutely and in kind; but *why?* The answer eluded him, and was lost, anyhow, in a renewal of desire as he laid the photograph on the table and began buttoning his overcoat. Oh, I *wish* she were my daughter, he kept thinking, and as he saw her clear unswerving eyes still fixed on the photograph, he thought further: There's something in you that means all that I've been meaning, all those ideas I've been trying to spread, everything I've been groping for in a blind way for years...

"Well," he said, smiling at her.

She moved back to the mantelpiece and stood again with her heels on the fender-rail. "Must you go?" she said, casually.

"Well...it's late, isn't it?"

"I'm going to make myself some coffee before I go to bed.

"I think perhaps--"

"It's probably too late for you to find a taxi in the streets. There's a telephone in the other room--I could ring for one when you wanted it."

"Well..."

"Take off your coat for a few minutes. I'll light the fire. After all, they told me to make myself comfortable, didn't they?"

She knelt on the rug to strike a match, and the gas-fire lit with a loud pop. When she rose he saw that her eyes were wet with tears. "I'd--I'd much rather--you didn't go till--till I've made you some coffee," she said, in a level voice.

"All right," he answered cheerfully. He took off his overcoat and almost flung himself into one of the deep armchairs that lay about. "I agree with you," he added, with a sort of forced nonchalance, "this room does make one feel at home. You'll have a job to turn me out of it if you're not careful." He laughed and she laughed also, and then went out to the little kitchenette that adjoined the studio.

CHAPTER NINE - SATURDAY MORNING

He lounged by the fire while she made coffee. A certain outward excitement died down in him, and he began to feel very cosy and tranquil and quietly talkative, so that when she brought the coffee and sat opposite him at the other side of the fire, they both plunged into chatter about the concert and music and other topics as casually as if the time and the place had been utterly normal. He felt, as he sat there, that he would like nothing better than for such a thing to happen after every long day of his life--to talk thus, and drink coffee, with her at the other side of a fire. It was something else in life that he had missed, and was now enjoying with all the more relish because till then he had never even guessed its existence--this pleasant comradely domesticity of two persons sitting up late to talk together after everyone else had gone to bed. A dreamy tenderness enveloped him as he gazed across at her; and gradually, in the midst of that tenderness, there grew in him the thought that she was beautiful. Like the lovely figurehead of a ship, he had imagined formerly, but now he imagined much more--she seemed to him rather like every beautiful thing there ever was or had been in the world--like Brahms, Raphael, William Blake...

They talked for over half an hour before he said he would have to go. "Really, I must--it's nearly half-past two, and I don't believe there's a night-porter at my hotel. I assure you I don't want to go a bit--I'm so comfortable here."

"Are you?"

"Yes, I'm hating the thought of going out into that cold street, but it's got to be."

"I'm hating the thought of you going."

"Yes, it's lonely for you by yourself. You're not nervous, are you, in a strange place?"

"No, no..." She seemed all at once filled with regret too intense even to try to conceal. "I'll go then and ring for a cab for you."

She hurried away and he heard her switch on the light in some further room. Left alone, he had a disconcerting vision of Browdley as it would await him on the morrow, of his prim and comfortless study, of the routine of weeks and months and years reaching into the future, of being an old man some day. Such thoughts induced him in a gloom which was all the harder to endure after his previous serenity--come now, he thought, as she returned, let's say good-bye and get it over quickly. "I think I'd better go down and wait in the street," he said, "the man will never find his way through that narrow entry. No, you mustn't come with me, it's far too cold. Don't bother to come down even--I'll let myself out. Thanks for the coffee. And remember what I said--if there's ever any way I can help you, write and tell me...The very best of luck...Good-bye, Elizabeth...Goodbye, my--my dear girl..." He did not look at her while he was speaking--come on, come on, he urged himself, don't linger and make it all more difficult...

Those few words; that quick handshake; and he was down the stairs, feeling for the door-catch. In another moment the door closed behind him and he stood shivering in the night air. He felt chilled and numb, with a little pinpoint of misery somewhere inside him that was expanding with every second. The world hung still and silent; it would take a minute or two, no doubt, for the cab to arrive. He paced up and down a short stretch of pavement, trying not to think, not even to feel.

Then, in the darkness of the yard whence he had come, a patch of light shone suddenly; he stared round, and saw her standing at the doorway. Never had his whole being swung into keener ecstasy than at such a reprieve--a few pitiful seconds snatched from an eternity ahead. He went back, trying to seem rather offhand and casual. "You shouldn't," he began, but he could hardly control his voice, "you shouldn't have bothered to come down. It's too cold for you to stand here. Do please go back. The cab will be up in a minute--there's really no need--"

"Come here," she whispered, clutching his sleeve. Dimly he wondered, and when she drew him into the little lobby at the foot of the stairs, the wondering grew to a tingling excitement. "That cab," he stammered, "I must keep a lookout for that cab...

"It won't come...Howat, I never rang for it...I couldn't--I found I couldn't...Are you very angry with me?"

The world dizzied about him, and he took her closely into his arms with all his senses brimming over. He did not and could not speak, but he knew bewilderedly that he had wanted her like that. After a moment, and without a word between them, they climbed the stairs and stood again in that warm, companionable room; it seemed full of welcome now. He took her to him again and the sweetness of her body streamed into his, and made him feel like a youth about to conquer the world. She clung to him with that strange, simple intentness that was in the way she talked and looked; he still could not think of any words, but she said to him, in a calm whisper: "I do love you so much, Howat. I can't help it. It began all the time you were giving me those lessons--all the time you weren't taking any notice of me. Of course it was absurd--that's what I told myself then--but now it doesn't seem absurd any more. It's everything else that seems absurd now."

"Yes, yes--I know." His mind was tremulously aflame at her confession, but especially at her mention of those earlier meetings; somehow the realisation that her love had come spontaneously and long before his, lifted him to a supreme pinnacle of rapture. "My dearest child..." he began, and meant to say such infinities of things, but found he could not progress beyond those few words. They drew away from each other then, and she went on talking in abrupt but still calm sentences. "Howat, I couldn't help it. I. tried, but it was no use. And I'm glad now that this has happened--yes, I'm glad, even if you aren't."

"But I'm glad too."

"Are you? You don't think you'll begin to hate me as soon as you get back to Browdley?"

He said then, only just audibly: "Impossible to do that--impossible...And as for Browdley--"

She watched him in gentle silence, and he saw the future dissolving into new backgrounds of such impossibilities. He felt as if he were sitting in the stalls of a theatre, seeing the curtain rise on the strangest and newest of plays, the play of the life which he himself had yet to live. He returned her gaze incredulously, and the thought came to him: Every day and night for so many years I have praised God with my lips, but now for the first time I praise Him with all my heart. He sank into a chair, silenced with thankfulness, and she came to him then; she sat on the arm of the chair and drew his head against her small firm bosom. "How tired you must be, Howat," she whispered. That enchantment of her bodily nearness soothed him; he did feel tired, but somehow eager as well, and he knew that he could rest, because she understood utterly both his eagerness and his tiredness. He closed his eyes and visions crowded on him--of music and painting and poetry and all the beauty of line and contour; a hundred sensuous images took meaning, while tunes raced through his mind with sharp unlooked-for harmonies; the whole world seemed on fire about him, while he, at its centre, found peace on the breast of this girl. "I can't go back," he stammered, huskily. "I can't...Do you realise that? Do you realise what you've done?"

"If I've done to you what you've done to me, then I'm glad."

"But I can't go back now! Do you realise that?"

"To your hotel? Well, it doesn't matter. You can stay here. We can talk. I'm not sleepy."

"It's--it's more than that I mean. Much more. I'm thinking of Browdley...Oh, Elizabeth, I wish I'd known you years and years ago!"

"Before I was born, that would have been!"

"Yes, I know. It's monstrous, I admit--a child like you and a man of my age. With a wife--children--and--and a chapel! My God, a chapel--think of that! Tell me, how much does all this mean to you? How long will it last? I want to know--is it just a fancy--the sort of thing you feel in the mood for after Brahms? How much exactly does it mean?"

She touched his forehead and then his hair with 'her fingertips. "Everything, Howat. There's only one thought in my mind, and that's how much I could be to you if you wanted me. Howat, I'm not afraid."

"*You're not afraid!*" He drew her to him exultantly and kissed her in the flush of splendour that her words had evoked. "Elizabeth, do you mean that-absolutely? You strange girl--you're so cool and calm all the time, and it's all so marvellous--the most marvellous thing that's ever happened to me. Do you think I could dare to let it go now?"

"Not if you feel certain that it's everything. *I'm* certain, in my own case, because I've never felt anything like it before. That makes it so simple. But you, of course--"

"And do you think I ever have, either?"

She gave him a single fearless glance that made him certain that there was nothing in his life beyond her instant comprehension. "Haven't you?" she said softly, and he shook his head, knowing that she would understand how true it was. Never before had there been in him this curious ache that made him feel almost raw with tenderness at the sight of her fingers stretched out on the arm of the chair or the delicate curving of her nostril or the little side-tooth that wasn't quite in line with the others. He said, abruptly: "You were right when you said I've not been happy. I've had some bad times. Did you ever hear about my two boys? One died when he was twelve--he would have been clever, I think, especially at music. The other, the elder, wasn't so clever, but he was a dear fellow--a bit wild at times, but there was no harm in him--oh, no real harm at all. He didn't like Browdley, and he was rather bored at home--we got him a job in a bank, but he wouldn't stay--he went off to Canada then--I haven't had any letter for three years. Perhaps I'll see him again sometime."

"You were very fond of him?"

"Yes." He added, fiercely: "He went off because he couldn't stand it. The routine of the bank, and then the routine of home life--the chapel services and everything else--I can see now, I ought to have taken his part more than I did. He told me, before he left, that he couldn't stand it. And I can't stand it now, either. The very thought of it turns me cold--to leave you and go back to that life--my God, I *can't* do it, Elizabeth. Do you think I ought to?"

"Do you think I want you to?"

"But ought I--*ought* I?"

"I don't think I'm ever sure what other people ought to do, Howat."

"That being more in my line of business, eh?" He laughed sharply. "It used to be, but it isn't any more. I've found myself out. I see my chance now, just as you see yours. I want to take it--oh, I want to take it so much--"

"And I want everything that *you* want--everything you could possibly want."

"I want *you*--I want--oh, my darling, we've only our two lives and they belong to us more than to any other person--shall we *run* for those lives of ours?"

"I know what you mean, Howat. I feel it, too--I feel it just like that--it's curious and rather dreadful, yet it makes me very happy." She stooped and laid her cheek against his. "I've thought of it all, as well as you--probably long before you did, really even to working out details. During dinner while we were talking I kept thinking of it all, though it seemed such absolute nonsense then." She smiled and went on softly: "I was imagining the two of us in Vienna together. Some big comfortable room with a piano in it, where you could compose when you felt in the mood, and I could fiddle away. And again later on, while I was making the coffee, I thought of it--a room perhaps something like this, though with a real fire for preference, and all kinds of interesting people dropping in at odd times to see us, and then afterwards, when they'd gone, being by ourselves--and drinking coffee--and talking--oh, plenty of talk--there'd always be that, wouldn't there? Howat, I can see it just exactly as it ought to be--why couldn't it all happen to us?"

He turned to her with a look of worship; he too was entranced by the imagined picture of that room, and as for the music he would compose, it was in his cars already. "It shall happen," he whispered, and there stole over him again that divine tenderness for her, making him aware, even had he not earlier guessed it, that there was still something more; it was not enough to have found the meaning of love, since on the very crest of discovery a further peak swung into view.

He kissed her and whispered again, with this new certainty of desire: "It shall happen," and felt her tears warm and then cool upon his face.

Later he began to tell her about his early life at Kimbourne...

It was early in the century when he had first arrived there. He was sixteen then, a tall thin youth wearing a grammar-school cap of exuberant hues that aroused the liveliest conjectures in the little Kentish village. His father, after losing money in rash speculation, had been killed in the South African War, and his mother had survived her husband by barely a year, having tried vainly in the meantime to retrieve the family fortunes by running a seaside boarding-house. The lawyer who wound up the estate had not known quite what to do with Howat; he thought him a nice-looking and decently-educated youth, but rather young to be flung into the world entirely on his own; clearly it would be a good thing if he could be got into a family for a few years; he would probably earn his keep, at least, as soon as he was put to work. It so happened that about that time the lawyer was visiting a client of his, a Mr. Coverdale, who was noted as a very religious and philanthropic person; he mentioned Howat's case, and Coverdale suggested that the boy should come along to Kimbourne, at any rate for a short holiday.

Howat walked from the station on a blazing June afternoon. Coverdale's house was about a mile out of the village a pleasant detached property with verandahs and low windows and a big garden full of flowers; the path from the garden gate to the porch was through an avenue of tall hollyhocks. Howat was hot from the walk, and he was also very shy. The house seemed grand to him after the miserable boarding-house basement, and he felt shyer than ever when a rather plump and cheerful-looking woman introduced herself as Mrs. Coverdale and asked him if he had had tea. He said no, and she took him into a room which, to his rather faltering eyes at that first sight of it, seemed entirely full of girls.

There were, indeed, seven of them, and they were presented one after another. Howat was struck almost completely dumb; he had never had anything to do with girls, and didn't know in the least what to say to them. He merely answered their questions when they asked if the train had been late, and whether he liked the hot summer; for the rest of the time he sat silent and uncomfortable. They chattered loudly all around him, and he wondered if it would be very rude to ask permission to go to his bedroom and wash, but he was too nervous to do so, and he actually made up his mind to run away to London the following morning after breakfast. Soon, however, the girls disappeared in ones and twos, leaving him alone with Mrs. Coverdale. He was not so nervous with her; she had a very genial and easygoing manner, and asked him scores of questions about himself, what his tastes were, what subjects he had liked best at school, and so on. He told her he liked music, and she said: "Ah, Mr. Coverdale will want you to play the harmonium this evening, then." The thought of that made him nervous again, and he wished he had said nothing at all about music.

Towards seven o'clock a mysterious imminence made itself felt in the atmosphere; there was a good deal of scurrying about on the part of the seven girls, and at a certain moment one of them, who had apparently been looking out of an upstairs window, called out: "Father's coming!" A few moments later a rather elderly man, grey-haired but very upright, walked briskly between the two rows of hollyhocks and entered the house. He kissed his wife and each one of his daughters very loudly, and then, on being made aware of Howat's presence, said gruffly: "How do you do, my boy?" and shook hands with him. After that he led the way to the dining-room and said a slow and solemn grace. There was little talking during the meal; sometimes he made a remark to which someone gave answer, but there was none of the chatter that had made the tea-table so noisy, and even Mrs. Coverdale did not seem in such an easy-going mood.

Afterwards she mentioned that Howat had confessed to being 'musical,' and sure enough, Mr. Coverdale suggested that he should 'play a tune' on the harmonium. For this purpose he was conducted into a very primly furnished drawing-room, full of stuffed birds and china ornaments; he was terribly nervous with all the family crowding round him, and more especially because he had never played a harmonium before. At first he failed to realise that he had to work the pedals, and even when he had made this important discovery he found that some of the notes wouldn't sound, and that a rather rapid Chopin study hardly suited the peculiarities of the instrument. He made what he felt to be a complete hash of the whole thing, but to his surprise and relief everyone appeared delighted, and Mr. Coverdale even went so far as to thank him in a deep booming voice.

A fortnight later it was somehow or other settled that Howat's holiday should not come to an end in the normal way, but that he should take up a permanent position in the Coverdale household.

Mr. Coverdale, indeed, thought the boy might 'do pretty well', and this, from such a source, was high enough praise. He had been a little prejudiced against him at first for having been brought up 'Church of England', but he soon found that the boy was intelligent, well-mannered, and ready to work hard. Mr. Cover-dale owned a saw-mill and timber-yard adjoining Kimbourne station, and it was not difficult to find ways in which the boy, by working eight or nine hours a day, could thoroughly earn the weekly half-crown which, in addition to his keep, became his initial wage.

Mr. Coverdale was a strict employer, but he was a strict man altogether; he neither drank nor smoked; he would literally have shrunk from touching a pack of cards; and his dislike of strong language went so far as to bring even such phrases as 'good heavens' under the ban. Every Sunday, without fail, he preached long and lugubriously eloquent sermons in little dissenting chapels scattered over the surrounding districts; some of these engagements involved journeys of ten or a dozen miles, and he would always make these on foot and in all weathers, disdaining even to saddle a horse, much less to make use of the unhallowed Sunday train service. Fortunately, he was a man of strong constitution and excellent physique; it was his boast, made with due thankfulness, that he had never had a day's illness in his life.

Howat did not dislike him even from the beginning, and soon came to be quite comfortable at Kimbourne. After a week or so he knew all the girls by sight and by name, though he was still rather nervous of them; the eldest, Lavinia, was hardly a girl at all; she was twenty-four, which seemed to him an immense age. It was Lavinia who kept the others in order, but Howat, if his shyness permitted him to have any active preferences at all, liked the younger ones better; the youngest of all was Mary, aged fifteen. He felt rather more drawn to Mary because she was only a 'kid', and was a good deal bullied by the elder girls.

Life would really have been very pleasant, but for Sunday, which came as a day of gloom after the comparatively cheerful activities of the working week. On Sunday no newspapers or ordinary books were allowed to be read, though if Mr. Coverdale's preaching engagements were at a distance it was sometimes possible to persuade Mrs. Coverdale to unlock the bookcase after he had gone. When, however, as very often happened he was occupied locally, the day progressed from morn to evening according to a most rigid routine. The whole family trooped out twice to the bleak little chapel at the Dover end of the village and filled up the pew immediately under the pulpit. Howat usually sat at one end and Mrs. Coverdale at the other, with the seven girls in between. He did not exactly enjoy the services, which seemed to him cold and uninteresting compared with the ones he had been used to, but there were times when Mr. Coverdale's rough eloquence stirred him to a vague self-scrutiny; and in any case, he always liked the singing, for he was beginning to develop a good voice and enjoyed using it. Then one Sunday the organist failed to appear, and Howat was asked, in an emergency, to play the hymns. He did so, fairly well, and when, some months later, the organist died, the boy was officially appointed in his place.

It was only an old and very wheezy American harmonium, but in it Howat found something to make Sunday a day to look forward to; he enjoyed particularly the opening and closing voluntaries, which gave him a chance of showing what he could do. Usually he played one or other of the simple pieces that had been left behind by the previous organist, but one morning, in a mood of great daring, he ignored the music sheet before him and made up something of his own as he went along. Rather to his astonishment no one complained or even appeared to notice any departure from the normal; and thus emboldened, he made a fairly regular habit of such improvisations. He did not, though, tell anyone about it.

After be had been at Kimbourne a year Mr. Coverdale increased his wage to ten shillings a week, and declared himself 'quite satisfied with him.

Those were the years when Howat was growing up, and when every month, almost every day, marked new and noticeable development. He was a rather quiet boy, good-looking in a thoughtful way, and he had very fine and striking eyes. He was not, however, particularly observant or knowledgeable, or he would have been aware that at least three of the Coverdale girls were head over ears in love with him. Lavinia, the eldest, considered she had a prior right to any attachment he might eventually make, and there were frequent quarrels between her and her sisters on this account. Howat, in fact, treated them all with complete impartiality, except that Mary, as still something of a kid, was admitted to more casual intimacies.

Howat's chief thoughts at this time were all on one subject-- music. Since his very earliest days he had been entranced by tunes, and now, with advancing youth, the desire to explore the magic world of harmony became speedily a passion. After the discovery that he could improvise, he seriously set himself to study the technique of composition; and most evenings, if he had time to spare, he would go to the harmonium in the drawing-room and try over invented tunes of his own. The family believed him to be 'practising', but at last the secret had to come out. He had submitted a song in a competition run by a musical journal, and had received the second prize of a guinea. The cheque arrived one morning at breakfast-time, and his delight was quite impossible to hide. When they all learned the truth, they were rather mystified; it seemed odd to them that Howat should have been able to pick up actual money in such a peculiar way.

One effect the disclosure had was to remove any further need for secrecy; henceforth all Howat's musical work was carried on openly. Some of the girls had mediocre voices, and Howat sometimes composed songs for them; but this was never much of a success, and the girls only bothered about it because they enjoyed the intimacy with Howat which trying over the songs involved. Even Lavinia, who had no voice at all, tried to develop one so as not to be at a disadvantage in this respect.

Howat was happy enough. He had come gradually to like as well as to respect Mr. Coverdale, and the old man, in his turn, had begun to feel for the boy an affection all the deeper because he had always wished for a son of his own. The family did nit know, and would perhaps hardly have credited, the terms upon which the two worked together at the timber-yard. Howat's job had developed into a sort of informal private secretary ship, but there was not always much work of that sort to be done, and sometimes in the afternoons they would sit together in the little matchboard office amidst the smells of glue and sawdust and hold most solemn discussions. There was something very impressive about the old man; with his white bushy hair and bright almost jet-black eyes, he looked rather like Howat's conception of an Old Testament patriarch. Howat soon perceived that the saw-mill and timber-yard were utterly secondary considerations with him; he ran them efficiently and conscientiously 'enough, but his real interest in life, and more and more as he was growing older, was religion. There was no doubting the sincerity of that religion, or that it was vastly more than a one-day-a-week affair. It steeped Coverdale's whole life, not precisely in happiness, but in a sort of wild and stupendous triumph. Once when Howat heard a certain theme of Beethoven's he thought instantly that it reminded him of Coverdale's attitude.

Howat was always very sensitive and impressionable, and the fervent booming eloquence of the old man, both publicly and in private, easily stirred him emotionally. Coverdale had, indeed, a noble though undisciplined command over English; he could paint the joys of heaven and the pains of hell in language which filled Howat's mind like great chords of music. The girls were all apparently unmoved by it, but often when Howat raised his head in chapel at the close of one of Coverdale's long prayers, his eyes were dim with tears. He always felt that the prayers had been framed to apply to himself personally, and though he knew that this was absurd, he could not get the idea out of his mind.

One day a curious incident took place at the saw-mill. A workman had been censured by Mr. Coverdale for using bad language;

Coverdale had had him up in the office and, in Howat's hearing, had delivered a long and impressive harangue on the sinfulness of such conduct and on the possibility that Providence might inflict sudden and condign punishment on anyone guilty of it. A few minutes after the man had returned to his work loud screams sounded from the saw-mill; Howat and Coverdale both rushed down, and found that the of-fending machinist had had all the fingers of one hand taken off by the circular saw. After he had been removed to hospital, Howat fainted; the sight had been too much for him; and when he recovered he saw Coverdale kneeling by his side with a fiercely triumphant light in his eyes. He was convinced that Providence had spoken through the me-dium of the ghastly affair, and into Howat's ears he poured there and then a terrific exposition of his own religious feelings and convictions. It was then that he told Howat that he prayed every night that the boy might 'get' religion as he had 'got' it, and might come to realise that there were more serious things in life than experimenting with little bits of tunes. Howat was touched and moved by the revelation that Coverdale thought so much about him and his future; and when the old man suggested that they should both pray aloud and in turn for the quick recovery of the injured workman, Howat, who was in a rather dazed mood, agreed. After a little preliminary nervousness when it came to his turn, he found that the words sprang to his lips quite flu-ently; he had listened to so much of Coverdale's eloquence that mere imitativeness, if nothing else, could have carried him along. He found the experience rather exhilarating in a way; he enjoyed the conscious-ness of control over language; it was rather like the first zestful sensation of riding a bicycle. When he had finished Coverdale signi-fied a grave approval; he was convinced, from that moment, that the boy was destined to be the means of saving innumerable souls.

Gradually, after that, and to a degree that Howat hardly real-ised, Coverdale's influence over him deepened and became more dominating. The day came when Coverdale at last persuaded him to use his 'gift of tongues' in public; he was very reluctant, but at last consented. It was a meeting held in the chapel schoolroom to raise funds for a new organ, and Howat, as organist, felt that there was some small excuse if he chose to say a few words on such an occasion. When he first stood up before that audience of forty odd people he was so nervous he could scarcely enunciate a word; his mouth began to twitch; and Lavonia's eyes, staring at him from the front row, seemed to transfix him into stupor. He did, however, manage at last to begin, and after a few halting sentences found himself escaping into some extraordinary upper air in which words came pouring on him, copiously and without effort. He spoke for ten minutes, and those ten minutes established his fame far more thoroughly than any of his tunes had done. The family, in particular, were thrilled to the point of hero-worship. They had never been able to comprehend the significance of his musical activities, but his eloquence, modelled on that of Mr. Coverdale, but delivered with such a refreshingly youthful and pleasant-sounding voice, seemed to them convincingly successful.

He was nineteen then, and a youth for whom in that little world of Kimbourne, the future seemed large with promise. There was a world, however, beyond Kimbourne, which he still privately inhabited, and even this world, to some extent, gave him encouragement. He bought himself a violin, and learned to play it moderately well; but it was not so much his intention to become a skilled executants as to master the technical possibilities of stringed instruments. In that twentieth year he began to compose pieces for violin and piano; he even tried his hand at trios and quartets, and a string quartet of his actually won a ten-pound prize at a London musical festival, and was performed once at a special concert. Kimbourne knew little of this, and the family, though they knew, were much less interested in it than in the verbal eloquence with which Howat could occasionally be persuaded to deluge them. For his successful first speech had naturally led to others, even to short addresses in the chapel; he found that he rather liked talking in public when once he got over the initial nervousness that always assailed him; it was the same sort of enjoyment that he derived from improvising on the organ or on the schoolroom piano to which he now had permanent access--all his speeches were, in a sense, improvisations on a theme. Success did not make him conceited, though he was human enough to enjoy sometimes the fulsome flatteries that were showered upon him; he was still very shy and rather unapproachable by strangers. But it was true, in a literal way, that he liked the sound of his own voice; and no wonder, for that voice, both in talking and singing, was a vibrant baritone which perfectly matched a face of singularly tender and thoughtful handsomeness. All the Coverdale girls were now more or less in love with him, even including Mary, and he was still entirely unaware of it. Even the prettiest girls in the village (which the Coverdale girls certainly were not) found him disappointingly aloof and unsusceptible.

At last he made a further surrender to Cover-dale's fervent pleading, and conducted a whole Sunday service--prayers, sermon, hymns, organ voluntaries, everything. As a one-man show it would in any case have been a noteworthy exhibition of versatility; but it was actually much more than that--so much more that it is possibly remembered to this day by some of the older inhabitants of Kimbourne. It happened that a massacre of workmen had just taken place in St. Petersburg, and Howat's sermon was a spirited attack on autocracy which brought the small assembly dangerously near to cheering point; Coverdale felt that there should have been more religion in it, but as a strong Liberal in politics, he could not but approve of the boy's sentiments. One effect of this rather astonishing outburst was to attract the attention of the local Liberal party organisers, and during the general election campaign a year later Howat made many speeches throughout the constituencies. By that time he had become a recognised local preacher, and the chapels in which he preached were always crowded with folk who came, many of them, to savour the novelty of a youth of twenty who could, as was said, 'let go as well as all the rest of them put together'.

Coverdale's dream was now that Howat should ascend to far loftier pinnacles than that of mere preaching in country chapels. He saw in the boy a coming Spurgeon, and he wished him to have all the benefits that the completes religious training could provide. His idea was that Howat should spend a few years at a college for prospective ministers, and then astonish the world by eloquence made more tumultuous than ever by means of book-learning; the old man, whose education had been entirely self-acquired, had a pathetically simple belief in the efficacy of study and collegiate life. To Howat, however, the whole idea did not especially appeal; he was not keen on becoming a full-time professional minister, nor did he wish to give up helping Coverdale at the saw-mill. He liked sermonising as a sort of hobby, but he was not sure that he wanted more of it than that. A good many of his friends, too, were urging him to take up a political career, and several constituencies were nibbling at him as a prospective Liberal candidate for the next election.

Then, quite suddenly, Coverdale had a slight stroke. For the first time in his life he had to resign himself to the ways of a semi-invalid; the doctor said he would probably recover, but would never be the same again, and would certainly have to sacrifice the cast-iron routine to which his life had up to then been dedicated. To Coverdale this meant only one thing; he would have to give up the saw-mill, since he would not, while there was breath in him, neglect his religious duties. Unfortunately Howat, though a hard and willing worker, had no aptitude for business and could not, it was clear, take on the job of management; but at that time, as it chanced, the profits were considerable, and it was not hard to obtain a satisfactory offer of purchase from a big joinery firm in Maidstone. The deal was put through; the Coverdale family found themselves with some thousands of pounds comfortably invested in gilt-edged securities, and Howat, of course, was out of a job.

That was in May of the year in which he had turned twenty-one. Coverdale, now a retired gentleman, passed most of his time at home, greatly to the family's discomfort; the immense seriousness of the problems of life and death weighed upon him more heavily than ever. He bought quantities of theological literature and studied it in a rather uncomprehending way; his mind was not attuned to subtleties, but he felt that the books would be very useful to Howat when he went to college. He had quite made up his mind that the boy should go, and Howat, with nothing else immediately in prospect, was also beginning to let such a future be taken for granted. Term began the following September, and the college, with which Coverdale had been in communication, had already signified its willingness to accept so promising an entrant.

But towards the end of June Howat went up to London for a concert; it would finish too late for him to return the same night, so he put up at a little hotel in Southampton Row which had been recommended him as cheap. It was the first time he had ever stayed overnight in London, and he was rather thrilled at being so completely on his own. The concert was not a public one; it was given by the students at a college of music, and Howat had been sent a ticket by a friend. A few men and girl students played Mozart and Haydn chamber music, not very marvellously, but with much enthusiasm, and afterwards there were ham sandwiches and lemonade and informal chatter round the piano. Howat got into conversation with several youths and was invited to join a party in somebody's rooms in St. John's Wood, close by; he went, and stayed there front eleven until the party broke up about three in the morning. As usual he was very shy at first, but after a time he found himself talking and discussing with the rest, and he even played over on the piano one or two of his own compositions, which were admired, though not excessively. A rather elderly man, well-known as a critic on a weekly paper, led him aside, however, and asked him if he intended to take up music composition seriously. "I don't want to give you a swelled head," he said, "but I think your stuff shows a certain amount of promise."

That night, as he walked from St. John's Wood to his hotel, with the first glimmer of dawn streaking the eastern sky, Howat saw the future clearly enough. He did not want to be a minister. He did not want to go into politics. His overwhelming triumphs in the pulpit and on the platform seemed tame and petty things compared with the very moderate amount of success he had so far achieved in the realm of music. He hated himself for having already wasted so much time. He felt that there was only one thing in life he could do, with any honesty of purpose; and that was to devote himself to the work that he loved, whether it would eventually bring success or not.

When he arrived at Kimbourne he made this decision known to Coverdale. He had guessed that the latter would be extremely disappointed, but he had scarcely been prepared for such a storm as ensued. Still less had he conceived it possible that Coverdale, in the heat of his excited protests, would have another and more serious stroke, rendering him speechless and partly paralysed.

During the days that followed, Howat spent hours at the old man's bedside, stared at by quivering eyes that now, in default of words, had to perform the whole function of expression. Howat was stirred as he had been years before, on the occasion of the saw-mill accident; only now he felt a personal remorse; he knew that he had given Coverdale what might prove a deathblow. The odd thing was that no one else knew this; no one had heard the argument; no one suspected that Howat had changed his mind about the training college. If only the others had known all about it, Howat could have defended himself; after all, it hadn't been really his fault--surely he had a right to please himself about his own future. But as he watched Coverdale through so many hours, he began to be oppressed with an emotion profounder than such comforting assurances; he began to doubt whether, after all, he had done right in flouting the old man's wishes; and he heard again, as in a dream, the Beethoven chords that stood for the grandeur and magnificence of Coverdale's beliefs. Remorse blackened and deepened upon him, and one afternoon, alone by the bedside, he was so moved that he knelt down, took Coverdale's hand, and asked for forgiveness. He would go to college, he said, and would become a minister. The look in Coverdale's eyes, instant and revealing, came to him then as a directly approving answer from Providence.

A kind of frenzy swept over Howat during that summer. He was definitely booked to enter college in September, and in the meantime he sought, with every atom of strength that was in him, to make amends for the harm he reckoned himself to have done. His sermons and prayers in the little chapels rose to impassioned intensity; he gave up all his political work, and took a leading part in an evangelist revival that was being conducted in the district. All this was reported to Coverdale and so encouraged his partial recovery that by August he was able to speak again, though slowly and with difficulty. His first words were to utter a prayer of thankfulness that Howat had at last 'seen the light'.

Howat, in fact, was in an almost hysterically emotional condition and overworked himself dangerously; he discontinued all his music composition because he found that the revival he was assisting in left him no time for it; yet somehow, rather to his dismay, he discovered that he could not escape it altogether; casual airs and tunes often obsessed him when he walked hone at evening across starlit fields; all kinds of things, moreover, seemed to excite him emotionally in a way he had never exactly experienced before--the sight of sunset over the long ridge of the Downs, the distant hoot of a steamer entering harbour at night, the smell of hay in the noonday lanes. Sometimes at twilight he passed lovers strolling side by side, and though they presented no novel phenomenon, he was aware of them now, for the first time, as part of the strange insurgent problem to which only religion, he felt, could supply an answer. He was dimly conscious that love must be a very lofty and spiritual thing, and he was sure that if he ever loved a woman, it would be in such a way.

Mary was then almost twenty. He had always been more intimate with her than with any of her sisters, some of whom he now almost disliked; they were silly, he had discovered, and shirked the main seriousness of life. Three, anyhow, had definitely given up all hopes of him and had accepted the attentions of other young men; Howat would occasionally find them loitering in the garden late at night, caressing and being caressed in a manner which seemed to him unnecessary as well as disagreeable. Lavinia was still unattached; she was too busy about the house to have time for that sort of thing, she said; for now Mrs. Coverdale also was in failing health, and a good deal of domestic responsibility fell on the eldest girl. Fortunately she was the type that could well shoulder it--a brisk, managing young woman, hardworking and capable, except that she did not cook very well. Howat now liked her perhaps best of the lot, next to Mary.

He liked Mary because, of all the seven, she was the only one who appeared to him in any way spiritual. Formerly he had appreciated her as a 'kid'; now it was as if at one clear bound she had acquired womanhood, but womanhood of a rather special kind. Even physically she was marked out from the rest; she had none of that tendency to plumpness that was a family trait. Really, she was not at all strong; she was nervous (Howat was nervous, too), and little things often upset her in a way that drew his particular sympathy. Moreover, she was deeply interested in his religious work; she attended all his meetings and services most assiduously, and during homeward walks she talked earnestly, if a shade ingenuously, about the more momentous concerns of life. On the night before he left for college, after a very prolonged and emotional talk with Mr. Coverdale, he asked her calmly if she would marry him when he had finished his training, and she answered, instantly but with equal calmness, that she would...

Most of this, so far as he was able to recollect it, Howat told Elizabeth as they sat by the studio fire throughout that November night.

About five o'clock they wakened after fitfully dozing in arm-chairs...

She prepared a small meal (they were far too excited to be very hungry), and by dawn were in the streets. It was bitterly cold, and there was a bleak, scouring easterly wind with a hint of snow in it. Everything had been planned and discussed; it only remained to put into execution all the strange things that had been decided on. The first Howat did without delay; he called at his hotel, retrieved his luggage, paid the bill for the room, and gave the proprietress (who was not really interested) some shadowy reason for not having occupied it. So much had been easy, but the next thing, though it seemed at first only a detail, gave much more trouble--the question of passports for the journey. Elizabeth had hers, of course, but Howat did not possess one at all, and the matter proved full of complications. He had the necessary photographs taken at a shop in the Strand as soon as it opened, but then came the business of having them endorsed by someone who knew him. He rushed to Blenkiron, in Wimpole Street, but found the doctor had gone away for the week-end; failing him, and after much cogitation, the nearest person he could think of was a minister, living near Kettering, whom he had not seen for six years. It meant a journey, but it had to be done, and he would probably be back in time to have the passport made out before the office closed that afternoon--then they could cross by the night boat and be in Paris the following morning.

It was settled that they should go to Kettering together, because they were in the mood of children; to have been separated even for those few hours would have seemed intolerable to both. They were wildly excited, but she, beyond her excitement, was calm enough to remember all the details of what had to be done; though it was he, perhaps, who was in the bigger hurry to get through them all. In the bus to the station he talked and laughed in sheer high spirits; he was a little drowsy, but it was the rapturous drowsiness of a small boy awakened early for some gloriously anticipated outing.

They caught the nine-fifty express with a few minutes to spare, and as soon as they were settled for the journey, in a compartment which they had to themselves, an attendant asked if they would take breakfast. Howat did not need to look long for her answer; they were both, it appeared, exceedingly hungry.

They passed along the corridors to the restaurant car and there commenced what Howat felt to be altogether the most delightful meal of his life. A thin film of snow had fallen during the night, enough just to cover the fields and roofs; bright sunshine struck tints of saffron into the pallor and a delicate unearthly glow came flooding into the train through the wide windows. As he watched her, he saw that it had turned her face to golden-brown; she looked lovelier to him than ever, and it was as if he were bathing all his nerves in that soothing loveliness. Even his sore throat, which had returned somewhat, he could now regard with toleration if not affection.

He was happy in an almost foolish way; he kept laughing and chattering and then falling half-asleep for a moment; and the smallest and most trivial things gave him infinite pleasure--because, for instance, he found he could have fish for breakfast as an alternative to eggs and bacon his eyes glistened like a child's. He felt, indeed, that in some secret way he had got back to childhood, that he was facing all life afresh, and with no anxiety save lest the years he was escaping from might somehow turn in pursuit. For the sake of that instinct rather than reason, he was feverishly eager to begin everything; he wanted to cross the Channel that night if it could possibly be managed, and she kept comforting him by talking about it and about the rest of the journey they would have. She was concerned for his tiredness and would gladly have spent another night in London, but he was passionately determined; and when she asked if he would not find three successive nights without proper rest rather fatiguing, he only laughed and answered: "I shall be perfectly happy on the train, unless you happen to know some kind friends in Paris who've gone off for the week-end and left their studio vacant."

That put them both in a mood of ecstatic recollection. "Oh yes, wasn't it extraordinary? Will you ever forget it, Howat? Even if I were never to see you again, I know I'd remember last night better than anything else that could ever happen."

"Yes, so would I. That curious way the clock stopped at seventeen minutes to four. Did you notice it? I suppose it was the sort that needs winding every night."

"We might really have wound it ourselves, mightn't we?"

"It would only have gone on for another twenty-four hours."

"Till we were over in France, perhaps." And there they were, back again at the irresistible topic. "We reach Dieppe about three in the morning, don't we? It's the cheapest route, and I don't mind a long crossing. At least I think I don't. I've been abroad once before, but only to Paris. We get there towards breakfast-time, I think. What shall we do if we have a few hours to spare? Have you been to Paris ever?"

"Once, years ago. I had the usual tourist's week. We'll stroll along the Boulevards, if it isn't too cold, and drink beer outside a café."

"And then we go through Switzerland, don't we, into Austria? I've never seen high mountains before. We go through Zurich and Innsbruck and Salzburg. What shall we do as soon as we get to Vienna?"

"Drive straight to the best hotel--if they'll have anything to do with us when they see our luggage. We'll afford it, for one day, anyhow. Then the morning after we'll search for that big room with the piano in it. And also, by the way, I shall have to buy some shirts and things. I won't have time in London to-night."

"What *fun* it's all going to be, Howat, as well as everything else!"

Just then they became aware of the grinding of brakes on the train-wheels, and she said, getting up: "I think we're slowing down for somewhere. We mustn't forget we've left things in the compartment--it's not the coats that matter, but those passport papers in the pocket of yours are really too precious...perhaps I'd better dash back and make sure that they're safe."

He answered: "All right. I'll attend to the bill and follow you along in a moment..."

She nodded smilingly and left him signalling to the waiter. Those were the last words he ever spoke to her.

EPILOGUE

One April evening Ringwood sat sipping his whisky and water in a very characteristic attitude. He was balancing himself on the edge of his pedestal desk, with his legs dangling and kicking the drawers, and his eyes directed over the edge of the tumbler in a rather quizzical stare. It was a favourite pose, though instead of a tumbler he would more usually hold up a medicine-bottle or a thermometer or a box of pills. The front of his desk was full of marks where he had been kicking it for thirty years.

To-night, however, the object of his scrutiny, though a patient, was also rather more than a patient. Ringwood was not quite certain how much more, but he knew, as he would have said, that he 'kind of cottoned on' to that chap Freemantle. He disliked parsons, as a rule (though no more than they disliked him); but Freemantle was an exception; you could talk to him; he wasn't stiff and starchy or shocked at a little strong language; and he had been particularly decent with young Trevis. Pity he had such a wife and that dreadful sister-in-law...

But Ringwood was puzzled. It was a week now since Freemantle had returned from his three months' rest-cure in Bournemouth, and every evening of that week he had called round at the surgery. Not that Ringwood minded, of course; he enjoyed a chat, especially if Freemantle wanted one; but the chats had not been the usual desultory discussions of politics and local affairs. On the contrary, Freemantle had seemed to have something on his mind all the time; he had kept harking back to matters which, Ringwood was sure, it was far better that he should try to forget altogether.

Ringwood, indeed, was just a little contemptuous of the newspaper fuss that had been made over Freemantle. It was all over now, of course, but at the time it had slightly irritated him. He disliked mob-emotion, and it seemed to him rather silly that a man should work hard and meritoriously for twenty years without any recognition at all and then suddenly leap into fame because of something perfectly accidental and irrelevant. Of course he'd behaved very pluckily; but wasn't there something rather fatuous in the way the Press and public had gone wild over him? It had been nothing less than disgusting, anyhow, to see those two women exploiting the poor devil as hard as they could go--that article, for instance, in one of the Sunday papers--"My Hus-

band, by the Wife of the Clergyman-Hero of Browdley"--it was ru-
moured that she'd been given a hundred guineas for it, and every word
had been written by a Fleet Street journalist. Disgusting...And Ringwood had thought, after reading it: God, I wish they'd give me a
hundred and five quid to write "My Patient, by the Doctor of the Clergyman-Hero of Browdley"--I wouldn't need to have it done for me; I'd
just tell the stark truth; I'd say: This chap's been slaving away at a
damned hard job for donkey's years, and that's why he's a hero, if he is
one, not because of a few hectic minutes after a railway smash...And
I'd also say: It's true he's had a bad breakdown, but that's not all
through doing the heroic stuff, as the mob likes to think--he was heading for trouble long before that, and if anyone wants to know the
reason, call at the Manse and take a look at those two damned women,
or three, counting the scraggy daughter...'

He drank a little whisky, and then resumed his gaze at the man
for whom, as much as for any person in the world, he felt a concern
mounting to affection. Yes, he did look ill, there was no doubt of that;
and his hand, his right hand, unfortunately, would never be much good
to him again; he had gone greyer, too, much greyer, since the affair.
The Bournemouth holiday had toned him up physically, but there was
a good deal, obviously, that was still wrong. Yet if the whole experience had been so terrible, as could well be believed, why did he want
to go on talking about it night after night, and to Ringwood only, it
appeared, out of the entire population of Browdley?

"Look here," Ringwood said, with more seriousness than was
usual with him, "why don't you drop it all, Freemantle? I can see how
it's still on your mind, and I can understand it's something you can't
easily forget, but why don't you try to? After all, you did your best,
and a damn good best it was--you've nothing to reproach yourself
with."

"Oh, I know..." Freemantle's quiet, troubled voice trailed off,
but his eyes continued to speak; and they were queer eyes, Ringwood
thought--indeed, he could almost agree with a sensational journalist's
description of them as 'haunted'. He thought to himself: We'll have
him going off his rocker yet if we're not careful...

"You see, Ringwood," Freemantle continued, you haven't
heard the true story. The newspapers got hold of everything but that."

"They seem to get hold of quite enough, if you ask me.
Frankly, in your place, I'd just drop the matter--"

"But I can't, Ringwood. I want to begin at the beginning--
before the newspapers came into it at all. Last night and for several
nights I've been trying to tell you, but somehow I couldn't get started.

But I've made up my mind to-night. I'll be happier afterwards. Do you remember, before I went to London, you said when I came back I was to report to you what sort of a time I'd had there?"

"Oh yes, I think I remember. I was only chaffing you, of course."

"Well, I've come to make that report now. You don't mind listening, do you? Am I taking up too much of your time?"

"Oh, Lord, no, don't think that. It's only that I feel...still, if you say it's going to do you good, fire away, by all means."

And Freemantle began, with what Ringwood at first took to be a mere irrelevance that would further delay the matter: "Do you remember that girl who ran away from home--Elizabeth Garland, her name was?"

Some little time afterwards, Ringwood interrupted: "Well, Freemantle, if that's your yarn, all I can say is, I don't quite know what you're being so dashed serious about. First you went to a specialist who diagnosed a sore throat--which I could have done for less than three guineas, by the way--then, feeling pretty bucked with life, you met this girl, and discovered that she wasn't, after all, eloping with a Jew old enough to be her father, but was off to Vienna on her own to study music. Personally I'd have thought the former project rather less of a risk, but that's by the by. Anyhow, you took her to dinner in Soho, and then went on to a concert. Quite the thing to do--I'd have done the same myself except that I'd have chosen a music-hall. Really, Freemantle, you don't expect me to be very shocked by this revelation of a parson's night out in the metropolis, do you?"

(Behind his banter, Ringwood was thinking: Wonder what they talked about, those two? Fearfully highbrow stuff, I suppose-- can't imagine Freemantle being very gallant--she probably thought he was rather sweet, but a bit of a bore--unless, of course, she was a bit of the same sort of bore herself. Must say, I can't abide 'arty' women at any price, but then, I'm not artistic, and as for music, I hardly know 'God Save the King' till I see people standing up...)

"I've more to tell you yet," Freemantle went on, deliberately. "After the concert we spent an hour or so at an hotel, and then, as it was getting late, I took her to the place where she was staying. It was a studio over a garage in Kensington--it belonged to some friends of hers. When we got there she asked me to come up and meet them, but we found the place empty. They'd left a note to say they'd been called away suddenly for the week-end."

"I see. So there you were, pleasantly parked with this girl in an untenanted studio?"

134

Freemantle took no notice. "She made some coffee and we sat and talked by the fire. I stayed on--talking--and--in the end--I didn't go back to my hotel at all."

"Didn't you, by Jove? Bit imprudent, eh? Supposing the studio people had come back unexpectedly?"

"I don't think we either of us thought about that. We were too absorbed thinking of other things. We--we discovered that--that we were both rather--rather desperately fond of each other."

Ringwood flushed slightly, not exactly from embarrassment, but because he felt he was going to be made a reluctant confidant in a matter which, for some reason, he would not be able to treat in any of his usual ways. Scores of times in that surgery men had confessed, as a rule shamefacedly, to some kind of amorous adventure, and scores of times he had kicked his heels against the desk and shouted at them, blusteringly: "Well, don't look so solemn about it--it's not the first time such a thing's been done in the history of the world, you know!" But with Freemantle an instinct warned him that his customary banter would not be appropriate; in his case there might be, after all, a certain seriousness. Ringwood, in fact, was just a little astonished; he hadn't really suspected Freemantle of being that sort of chap. Not that he thought any less of him for it; as a man; heavens, no--but really, you did somehow expect parsons to behave themselves a bit more than other people. Rather like the Wakeford case, in a way...

He said, after another gulp of whisky: "Look here, old man, I really don't see the point in your telling me all this. I'm not a father-confessor or a censor of morals or anything like that, but I do suggest, as a man of the world, that all that sort of thing is better not chattered about. Know what I mean, eh? Lots of things we all do that we shouldn't--naturally--but what I do feel is, Why tell people--why tell anybody?"

But you don't understand what I am telling you, Ringwood! There wasn't anything like that! We just talked--and talked--there was nothing--of the kind of thing you're suggesting--nothing at all--"

"All right, old chap, all right. Sorry if I dropped a brick." (He thought: Poor devil, does he really think anyone would believe that? And Ringwood reflected curiously upon the morbid mentality that would embark upon a totally unnecessary confession and then furiously deny the only thing that gave the confession any point at all.) He went on, almost gently: "My dear Freemantle, I still say--Why bother about it? Whether you did or didn't do this or that, what the hell's the use of arguing about it now? It's over and done with for better or worse--why can't you forget it with all the rest?"

135

But Freemantle still went on, and still with the same slow and inexorable emphasis: "I was telling you, wasn't I, that she and I had discovered that--that we--meant everything to each other. So--so we talked things over--and decided--in the end--to go and live in Vienna together."

"*What?* What's that?"

"Just as I said. And the next morning we--she and I--were going to Kettering, because I knew somebody there who would sign my passport papers--that was necessary, you know, before I could get away. We were having breakfast together on the train, and she'd just gone along to the compartment while I stayed behind a moment to settle the bill--I didn't even have time to do that--I never paid it, as a matter of fact--because the other thing happened so quickly...Now--*now* do you understand?"

Ringwood's heels banged against the desk. "What? I don't quite follow--what's that you're saying?"

"It happened--then--you see--while she was away--and I was staying behind...Don't you understand?"

"Good God, man, I've heard all you've said, but--but I can't grasp it--surely you don't mean--"

"Yes, yes, I do mean it. It's--it's a rather queer and awful thing to have happened, isn't it? But it's the truth."

"The truth!"

"Yes. The truth that the newspapers never guessed."

"You mean--that she--this girl you were travelling with--was *killed?*"

Freemantle answered quietly, but with his voice deep with horror: "She must have just reached the first coach when--it happened. I saw her there--amongst it all. I tried to get her out. I couldn't. She was burned to death. I *saw her...*"

His eyes took on a vivid glare, and Ringwood, even in the midst of his amazement, sprang to instinctive professional awareness. "Come, come," he said, putting down his glass and walking over to Freemantle. "None of that, now. No good, you know." He put a hand on the parson's swaying shoulders, and Freemantle seemed to derive strength from the contact. After a while he looked up with more tranquil eyes and said, with a sharp sigh: "Well, there it is. I've told you now. I'm glad somebody knows at last."

"My dear chap, yes..." Ringwood went to a cupboard and drew out his emergency bottle of brandy, but Freemantle waved it aside; he was all right, he said, now that he had told what he wanted to tell. He

136

added, plaintively: "I'm sorry, Ringwood, for wasting your time all the other evenings of this week."

"Oh, that's all right..."

"I must have been a terrible nuisance."

"Oh, nonsense..."

"Well...you can understand...now..."

"I'm trying to, anyway. But--but it's--it's all so damned extraordinary I don't know what to think. It's just about taken the wind out of my sails. D'you mean--I suppose you do--that nobody's got the slightest inkling of what's really happened?"

"Not the slightest, Ringwood. All the passport things were left in the compartment and were burned. Nobody who knew either of us had seen us on the train, and it happened to be a Manchester train that I might very well have been travelling on in any case. I was even using up the return half of my Manchester ticket. And she--she was wearing no jewellery--nothing that gave any clue--afterwards. Even her parents aren't curious--they've quite made up their minds that she's gone to the bad, and they neither expect nor wish to see her again."

"It's all most amazing. The most amazing thing I ever heard of in my life." A faint thought struck him and he added: "I suppose you've not been dreaming all this by any chance, have you, Freemantle?"

"Hardly."

Ringwood flung himself down in his swivel-chair and for a few seconds scribbled idly on his blotting pad, trying to absorb the intricacies of a situation to which all his years of experience could provide nothing approaching a parallel. He was not a very imaginative person, and he found himself more and more befogged as he pondered over it all. The only theory which to him, as a medical man, seemed to fit the case was that Freemantle might be completely off his head, and have invented the whole story with the fervid ingenuity of the mentally deranged. At last, throwing down his pencil, he exclaimed: "Well, if you say it all happened I'll have to believe it did, that's all. But what I chiefly can't fathom is this Vienna business. You say you had definitely made plans to go out there with this girl?"

"Yes. If the passport could have been arranged quickly enough, we should have left London that same Saturday evening."

"But what on earth would you have done when you got there?"

"She was going to study music. I was going to compose, if I could."

"*Compose?*"

"Yes. Compose music."

"Would it have brought in any money?"

"Probably not. I might have tried for some teaching job in a school. I could have taught English, perhaps."

"And what if you couldn't have found such a job?"

"Then I don't know how things would have turned out."

"Had you money?"

"She had nearly two hundred pounds, and there were a few shares and things I might have sold for a hundred or so. It would have been enough to begin on."

"To begin what on?"

"Our lives. To begin our lives on."

He said that with such simplicity that Ringwood was swept into still further bewilderment. "But good heavens, man, do you mean you were never going to come back at all?"

"Yes, probably that."

"But what about your wife--your daughter--and, for that matter, your chapel?"

"I felt that all that didn't matter compared--compared with the other thing."

"What other thing?"

"Something I can't exactly describe--I never could--but I saw it then--while I was with her."

Ringwood shrugged his shoulders with a gesture of profound bafflement. "You'd have had to be less vague than that to your wife when you wrote explaining things."

"I shouldn't have tried to explain. She wouldn't have starved-- she has money of her own. And as for caring, do you think she'd have cared a great deal, apart from the scandal?"

"But really, Freemantle, even if she wouldn't, you can't throw over your responsibilities in that casual fashion. It's preposterous!"

"I felt then that everything else was preposterous."

"You mean that you'd no doubts or misgivings of any sort?"

"I couldn't doubt anything that seemed so beautiful to me at the time."

"Seems to me, old chap, it isn't so much a question of what's beautiful or not beautiful as of what's right and what's wrong."

"I wonder if thinking that makes you really a more religious man than I am."

Ringwood shrugged his shoulders again; he was no metaphy-sician; his code was rough but simple. Much as he disliked Freemantle's wife, he was, though he would not perhaps have used the word, a little shocked at the idea of any husband so calmly deserting his legal partner. Casual adultery he could comprehend and excuse, much as he might deplore the bad taste of subsequent confession; it was human, in his view, compared with the chilly ruthlessness of Freemantle's Vienna proposition. He gave his nose a vigorous blowing and went on, rather gruffly: "Well, all I can say, Freemantle, is that to me the whole thing's still perfectly astonishing. Do you really believe you could have been happy for long in a foreign country with a mere girl you hardly knew?"

"Yes. Absolutely happy. And always."

A quarter of an hour later Ringwood had recovered something of his normal equanimity of mind. It was characteristic of him that he never worried for long over a problem; if it proved too much of a twister he merely gave it up, and passed on to the next. Freemantle's emotional altitudes were beyond him, and he felt, moreover, a sort of reluctant crossness over them; he preferred a discussion in territory where he knew a few signposts. He didn't want to preach; but there was, after all, a certain rough-and-ready morality which, as a man of the world, he felt it his duty to impart on rare occasions; and the more he thought about it, the more convinced he was that Freemantle was desperately in need of someone to give him a dose of good 'horse sense'. That was, of course, assuming that his amazing story were true; Ringwood could not yet make up his mind entirely about that. He noticed that Freemantle's face was very pale and that a rather unnatural and bloodshot brilliance was still in his eyes; he felt so confoundedly sorry for the chap, but what could one do--except give him sound advice? Completely mad, he must have been, Ringwood reflected, to be bowled over like that by a mere girl--attractive girl, though, with a deuced good figure, he remembered--and some excuse, perhaps, for any man with a wife like that and a sister-in-law bullying him all the time...But what was clearest of all to Ringwood was that it was the future that had to be faced, not a lot of had-beens and might-have-beens. Ringwood's natural outlook on life soon cut through the tangle of Freemantle's position; he did not solve the problem; he just thrust it to one side in a you-be-damned kind of way, and with growing confidence gave the man's shoulder a few encouraging shakes. "Look here, old chap, you may think I've not been particularly sympathetic over all this, but believe me, I'm just about as sorry for you as anyone could be. I can quite understand how you feel about it all, but the fact is, you're rather bound not to see things as logically as a mere outsider can. That's natural, isn't it? Well, I'm the outsider, and I look at it rather in this way, if you don't mind d a very candid opinion--You've had a damned narrow escape!"

"*An escape?*"

"Yes. Don't you see what I mean? Really, though I wouldn't call myself in any sense a religious chap, there does almost seem a sort Providence in it--don't you feel that? At any rate, what's the harm in thinking so? You go and get yourself into the deuce of a hole and then, just as you stand on the very brink of the precipice Providence steps in and cuts all the knots for you, so to speak. Those are mixed metaphors, but you can see what I'm driving at. Don't you realise that you're being given a chance--a chance to put all that silly escapade on one side as if it had never happened? Why, man, you've got half your life in front of you yet--think of it--think of the future--and if at odd times you do happen to recollect this queer business, call it just a mistake--a single solitary mistake that you couldn't help!"

"*A mistake?*"

"Well, we all make 'em don't we? And we're dashed lucky if we're given the chance of covering them up without a trace. Why, when you're as old as me, and you look back on a lifetime of decent honest straightforward doing-your-job, you won't bother much about a mad mood that happened in the midst of it all."

"Doing my job? What do you mean by that?"

"Why, your ordinary everyday parson's job, of course."

"Here--in Browdley?"

"Why not."

"You think I can carry on here--as if--as if nothing had happened?"

"Why not? You told me yourself that nothing did happen."

"Did I?"

(Ah, Ringwood thought, just as I suspected--anyhow, he's admitted it now--that's better than persisting in an absurd fairy-tale that nobody in his senses would believe--and, after all, there's nothing so very dreadful in it--she probably lured him on, anyway.) He replied, with growing cordiality: "My dear Freemantle, I understand all that of course, of course. But the point is, as I've been saying a good many times, it's what's going to happen that matters, not what did happen. Here you are, with all your roots, as it were, in Browdley, working well and doing quite a deuce of a lot of good--perhaps in a smallish way, but then, when you come to think about it, aren't all our ways pretty small? It's the small ways, anyhow, that keep the world going-- I'm certain of that. Well, here you are, as I said, and whether you know it or not, you're liked in this town, you're respected, even admired, and folks would damn well miss you. That's as much as can truthfully be put on most tombstones. You've had a dozen years of useful slogging away, and there ought to be at least twice as many ahead of you in the future--are you going to smash all that for the sake of a single incident that nobody knows or could ever know about unless you tell them?"

"Some of the biggest things that have ever happened have been single incidents."

"Nonsense!" replied Ringwood, stoutly, in haste to check any further plunge into abstract philosophy. "Believe me, nothing's forgotten more quickly than a week-end flirtation, however much you think it means at the time...The point is, once again, that you've been given this chance to carry on, and you've jolly well got to take it. D'you suppose other people haven't got Secrets in their pasts? See, here's a little yarn about myself--it's the sort of story most doctors could tell, no doubt, only they don't--no more would I, except to convince a chap like you. It happened about five years ago; I was called in to attend to two kids with the measles--ordinary working-class family, you know-- no nurse or anybody like that to look after them. Well, they didn't have it very badly, and all seemed to be going along quite normally when one afternoon I was sent for in a mighty hurry--those two kids had suddenly got worse. I went along and found--to make the story short-- that somehow or other in mixing up the medicine for them I'd come an awful cropper--I'd put loads of strychnine in by mistake--heaven knows how I'd managed to do it, but there it was. My God, I worked pretty hard, that day--I was at the house till nearly midnight, trying to rinse out the stomachs of those kids. The boy kicked the bucket, but I managed with the girl. Well, what d'you suppose I did then? Blabbed it all to the first person I met? Not a bit of it--I said to myself: Ringwood, this is a nasty business, but mistakes will happen--it's the first of this kind you've ever made, and with luck it'll be the last. You do more good than harm on balance, and that's as much as can be said of most men. So I just signed 'measles' as the cause of death on the certificate and that was that. The kids' mother swears by me--she tells everyone how I slaved away for hours trying to save their lives--nobody could have done more, she says, which is true enough, by Jove. I'm not Inventing that, Freemantle--I once actually overheard the woman praising me to the skies at a street-corner...I suppose it seems a terribly immoral story to you? Perhaps you think I ought to have phoned the coroner and confessed to manslaughter?"

"No, no--I don't blame you."

"Well, isn't it the same sort of thing in your case?"

They talked for a little time longer, but Freemantle seemed exhausted, and Ringwood, too, felt that the argument might prove all the more effective if it were now curtailed. When Freemantle rose to go, Ringwood wanted to drive him home, or at least walk with him, but Freemantle said no; there was no need; it was bright moonlight; and Ringwood had an impression he rather wished to be alone to think things over. "Just as you prefer then," he answered, jovially, and gave the parson a hearty handshake at the surgery-door. "Good-bye, old chap, remember what I've said."

Howat walked slowly along the High Street, trying to remember what had been said by both of them, but hardly a word or a sentence of the long discussion came to memory. All he could see and think of was that silver slope of the roofs as the moonlight streamed upon them, and the pale glare that filled the middle of the roadway. He was more tranquil in mind than he had been for many days, but it was the moonlight making him so, he felt--not anything that had been said that night. And yet he was glad to have had that talk with Ringwood; he liked the doctor--a thorough good fellow.

Just one small matter was still on his mind, even when all else had been pacified; he was aware, though dimly, of having forgotten something--some time ago--yet not so very long ago, really--what was it, he wondered? He had been wondering for many days and had often felt himself on the brink of recollection; and now, all at once, as he was turning the corner from the High Street into School Lane, he remembered; it was those evening papers he had promised to bring back for Trevis. Only a little thing, but he felt helplessly sorry about it; it was the one thing, of all things, that stirred him to real remorse. Perhaps he might visit Trevis in the morning.

And suddenly then the whole familiar routine of life swung into focus and became once more possible. The meetings and services and committees and what not, the daily hours in the study and the visits to old ladies and the baptisms and weddings and funerals and all the rest of it--there it was, facing him inexorably, but somehow with the beauty of that night around it all, lending it a rich and fragrant hopefulness. That factory over there, black against the sky, but with all its windows gleaming, and that line of workmen's cottages pushing out into the sea of moonlight like a long black jetty, and the tramlines shimmering into the distance as he crossed the road--lovely, lovely, all that was. He hummed a tune that was in his head--ah, that thing of Brahms again--strange how it seemed to fit in with everything he felt. How short life was, and how brief the moments in it that really mattered! Nor could the framework of years enclose such divine fragments; they were timeless, notes in the never-finished symphony of the world. It was the quality of life that counted; forty years, a whole lifetime, could be as nothing weighed in the balance against a moment's lifting of the veil that hid beauty.

As he came within sight of his house and chapel a small boy passed by with a timid smile. Howat stopped and spoke to him in the friendly way he always had with children, and after a few shy answers the boy asked: "When are you going to tell us some more, sir, about the two little boys who sailed in a boat to an island?"

Howat was puzzled at first; he could not think was being referred to; but at length he called to mind that foggy afternoon when he had given his daughter's class a so-called geography lesson. He said, happily: "Very soon--perhaps this week," and gave the boy all the money he had in his pocket--four pennies and two half-pennies.

When he reached the Manse he found his wife waiting up for him in one of her less amiable moods; but of course she was so highly-strung--he knew it was really not her fault. "If you're well enough to stay gossiping with that man Ringwood until this hour," she said, with some asperity, "I should think you might begin on the pile of correspondence that's been waiting for you to answer for the last four months."

"Perhaps so, perhaps so," he replied softly, blinking his eyes to the light. "It's time I was back again at work, isn't it?" He gave her a very gentle smile and added: "If you like, my dear, you can tell Ellen to put a fire in the study to-morrow..."

You may also enjoy ...

Wandering Between Two Worlds: Essays on Faith and Art
Anita Mathias
Benediction Books, 2007
152 pages
ISBN: 0955373700

Available from www.amazon.com, www.amazon.co.uk
www.wanderingbetweentwoworlds.com

In these wide-ranging lyrical essays, Anita Mathias writes, in lush, lovely prose, of her naughty Catholic childhood in Jamshedpur, India; her large, eccentric family in Mangalore, a sea-coast town converted by the Portuguese in the sixteenth century; her rebellion and atheism as a teenager in her Himalayan boarding school, run by German missionary nuns, St. Mary's Convent, Nainital; and her abrupt religious conversion after which she entered Mother Teresa's convent in Calcutta as a novice. Later rich, elegant essays explore the dualities of her life as a writer, mother, and Christian in the United States--Domesticity and Art, Writing and Prayer, and the experience of being "an alien and stranger" as an immigrant in America, sensing the need for roots.

About the Author

Anita Mathias was born in India, has a B.A. and M.A. in English from Somerville College, Oxford University and an M.A. in Creative Writing from the Ohio State University. Her essays have been published in The Washington Post, The London Magazine, The Virginia Quarterly Review, Commonweal, Notre Dame Magazine, America, The Christian Century, Religion Online, The Southwest Review, Contemporary Literary Criticism, New Letters, The Journal, and two of HarperSanFrancisco's The Best Spiritual Writing anthologies. Her non-fiction has won fellowships from The National Endowment for the Arts; The Minnesota State Arts Board; The Jerome Foundation, The Vermont Studio Center; The Virginia Centre for the Creative Arts, and the First Prize for the Best General Interest Article from the Catholic Press Association of the United States and Canada. Anita has taught Creative Writing at the College of William and Mary, and now lives and writes in Oxford, England.
Website: www.anitamathias.com/
Blog: wanderingbetweentwoworlds.blogspot.com/

Lightning Source UK Ltd.
Milton Keynes UK
UKOW02f1950120115

244381UK00001B/279/P